A COMPELLING CASE FOR CLINICAL DOCUMENTATION

A Compelling Case for Clinical Documentation

Volume 2

Use the CAMP Method to Improve Clinical Documentation Quality

Ruthann Russo, PhD, JD, MPH, RHIT

DJ Iber
PUBLISHING

A Compelling Case for Clinical Documentation by Ruthann Russo

Published by
DJ Iber Publishing, Inc.
One Bethlehem Plaza, Suite 1010
Bethlehem, PA 18018
www.djiber.com

Two-volume set: ISBN 978-0-9799061-3-8
Voume 1: ISBN 978-0-9799061-5-2
Volume 2: ISBN 978-0-9799061-6-9

Library of Congress Card Number: 2008907257

Editor: Ginger McQueen
Cover Artist: Emmalea Russo
Technology Consultant: David Moore
Cover and interior design: Concord Editorial and Design

Additional resources: *www.acompellingcase.com*

♲ Printed on permanent, acid-free paper. This paper contains 100% post-consumer waste fiber.
   Printed by Print Net, Inc., Pittsburgh, PA

Manufactured in the United States of America
10 9 8 7 6 5 4 3 2 1

Trademark Notice

The CAMP™ Method is a trademark of Ruthann Russo. By purchasing this book the buyer is permitted to utilize the methods and resources of the CAMP™ Method as presented in *A Compelling Case for Clinical Documentation* for training and education purposes only within the specific facility or organization in which they are currently employed. The CAMP™ Method and *A Compelling Case for Clinical Documentation* may not be utilized as the basis for commercial products, services, seminars, training sessions, or consulting engagements without obtaining a separate license agreement from Ruthann Russo and/or DJ Iber Publishing, Inc.

Contents

List of Figures

A Compelling Case for Clinical Documentation

Volume 2

Use the CAMP Method to Improve Clinical Documentation Quality

Introduction

CLINICAL DOCUMENTATION in the patient record is the common ground between the medical staff and healthcare managers. Physicians use the patient record as their primary communication tool with each other in order to treat the patient. All physicians use the existing patient record when they are following up with the patient. They also use it for research. On the other hand, the healthcare management team uses the patient record for legal, quality measures, risk management, and planning. Further evidence of this symbiotic relationship occurs when the physician's documentation is translated by hospital employees into coded data that is used to determine how much the hospital will be paid.

The patient record, and what it represents, is at the core of every healthcare encounter. The record is legal evidence that the encounter occurred. In a typical hospital visit, at least 14 different clinicians will document in each patient's record. And today, most patients are aware of their rights concerning their health information as a result of HIPAA regulations. A patient is three times more likely to ask for a copy of her medical record today than she was ten years ago. And that same patient is twice as likely to read and comprehend the information in her record than she was a decade ago.[1] So why not come to a meeting of the minds that is in everyone's best interest—most of all, the patient's—to keep this document as impeccable as possible?

It is surprising, given the importance of clinical documentation, that physicians are not trained to develop clinical documentation skills during medical school or residency. Healthcare managers need to take actions to compensate for this lack of training. Designing a training program that plays an important and necessary function for the organization is a good first step in this process. The initial and continuing training process is the core component of the organization's clinical documentation program.

The management of a clinical documentation program requires excellence in operations. However, unless the operationalization of the program is preceded by organizational commitment and woven into its ongoing strategy, the program is unlikely to succeed. Volume 1 of this book addresses the strategic components of a clinical documentation program, while this volume addresses how to operationalize and sustain a program through training and education. Initial and ongoing training components of the CAMP™ Method (*coaching, asking, mastering, and peer learning*) were developed specifically for training physicians on clinical documentation improvement. The tools needed to implement the CAMP method with your medical staff are included in this volume and the resource disc.

YOUR CLINICAL DOCUMENTATION VVMS

Prior to beginning a clinical documentation quality program, your organization developed a rationale, which we call the values, vision, and mission statement, for pursuing the program. Essentially, this statement answers the question: *Why are we interested in improving clinical documentation?* Whenever an organization is dedicating resources and money to an activity, it must justify that the activity is aligned with the organization's vision and mission statement. Then, in order to obtain optimal results from the program, a specific values, vision, and mission statement (VVMS) should be developed for the clinical documentation program. This statement should include what you value in documentation; how you envision documentation impacting the organization in the future (for example, impacting quality scores, patient care, etc.); and how you will design a process to arrive at that future state. Your VVMS is your guiding beacon throughout the implementation and operation of the program. You should refer to the statement when making any major decisions to ensure that the program operations are aligned with the vision your organization has for itself and for the program. This

Figure 1. Descriptions of Documentation Standards Provided to Physician Study Participants

Documentation Characteristic	Example/Description
Timely	Meeting time requirements imposed by law, regulation, or internal policy
Legibility	Required under all government and regulatory agencies
Completeness	All abnormal test results have documentation regarding clinical significance of the test result (JCAHO requirement)
Clarity	Unambiguous documentation, especially in the case of a symptom principal diagnosis: Instead of chest pain use GERD (if supported); instead of syncope use dehydration (if supported)
Consistency	Agreement between two or more treating physicians, or resolution of any conflicting documentation upon discharge
Precision/Detail	Specific diagnosis documented when it is supported (anemia vs. acute or chronic blood loss anemia)
Reliability	Treatment provided only with documentation of the condition being treated (Lasix, CHF documented; KCL administered, hypokalemia documented)

strategic alignment will offer your organization a greater likelihood of success and sustainability. You can find additional resources regarding development of a Clinical Documentation Improvement VVMS in volume 1 of *A Compelling Case for Clinical Documentation*.

DEFINITION

We often use the phrase *high quality clinical documentation* loosely. What one hospital or group defines as high quality clinical documentation may be quite different from another. The term *quality*, according to Six Sigma principles, is subjective to a certain extent since quality is defined by the customer. In an attempt to standardize clinical documentation practices, this book sets forth a definition of high quality clinical documentation derived from official and quasi-official resources, such as the Centers for Medicare & Medicaid Services (CMS), the Joint Commission (JCAHO), and the American Health Information Management Association (AHIMA). This definition encompasses the minimum data set for high quality clinical documentation; it is documentation that is: timely, legible, complete, reliable, clear, consistent (unambiguous), and precise. Descriptions are provided in figure 1.

PREPARING FOR THE TRAINING PROCESS

In 2007, I had the opportunity to spend an entire day with the cardio-thoracic surgeons at a major metropolitan hospital. The purpose of the training session was to educate the physicians about the importance of high quality clinical documentation. The ultimate goal of the program was to provide the physicians with some basic strategies they could apply on their own to improve documentation and to introduce them to the organization's clinical documentation program. The physician's role in the program was, first, to provide high quality documentation; and second, to respond to any questions asked about her documentation when, based upon clinical evidence in the record, it appeared the documentation did not meet one or more of the criteria for high quality clinical documentation.

I was concerned about a lack of physician engagement during the training. I had not anticipated the challenge that this physician group would pose. We encountered our first obstacle as we moved to the section of the training where the physician member of our team would take over the instruction. None of the surgeons, including the chief, was interested in listening. As we analyzed the dynamics between our physician instructor and the surgeons, it became clear that we needed to get the chief of surgery involved. Because all of the surgeons looked up to the chief, he was the only one they would listen to. We improvised by giving the chief the podium to lead the discussion while we sat at the table and talked through the slideshow about the documentation issues we had identified in some of their records. This simple change literally made the difference between success and failure. Certainly, this story illustrates the importance of understanding the dynamics within physician teams, and the ability to be flexible enough to make last minute changes, when needed, to compensate for unplanned events.

HOW PHYSICIANS VIEW MEDICAL RECORDS

Another challenge facing the management team charged with clinical documentation training is physician perception of patient medical records. Physicians are trained throughout medical school and residency to respond to acute patient emergencies. The patient is the primary focus for every physician. The documentation about what they did with the patient, what they thought, and how they will proceed, is considered by most to be secondary to the *real work* of the physician. However, when physicians were surveyed about their attitudes and opinions regarding medical records and clinical documentation, the two highest rated statements were: (1) *I believe that clinical documentation is important* (3.77 on a scale of 0 to 4) and (2) *I believe that feedback about my clinical documentation is important* (3.62 on a scale of 0 to 4).[2]

According to *Physicians' Views on Quality of Care*, physicians' most common problems with quality in healthcare all involved health information and lack of coordination of care. Issues impacting quality of care that were identified by physicians include the following:

- Patient's medical record, test results, or other relevant clinical information were not available at the scheduled visit
- Providers had to repeat tests or procedures because findings were unavailable or inadequate for interpretation
- Patient experienced a problem following hospital discharge because physician did not receive timely information from the hospital
- Patient care was compromised due to conflicting information from different doctors or other health professionals[3]

This survey reveals that physicians perceive the quality of clinical documentation as being problematic; they also believe that if it were improved, the improvement would result in higher quality care to patients. When physicians are made aware of how much the quality of clinical documentation impacts their *real work* of treating the patient, the quality of clinical documentation takes on added importance.

HEALTH INFORMATION MANAGEMENT– PHYSICIAN RELATIONSHIP BUILDING

Regardless of where the clinical documentation function is housed in your organization, it is essential for the health information management (HIM) department to have a positive and productive relationship with the physicians. The physicians will find themselves in the HIM department responding to questions about their clinical documentation that they did not respond to on the units. In this case, the physician is the customer of the HIM department. Just as with any customer relationship, you are more likely to obtain a timely and optimal response if you have a good relationship with the customer, who in this case happens to be the physician.

As a way to assess the HIM–physician relationship, this volume contains an assessment survey to be completed by all HIM managers and, if possible, some sampling of members of the medical staff. The survey for the HIM management team asks questions about:

- The respondents' knowledge of physicians as a group
- The respondents' knowledge of each physician's characteristics
- Formal communications
- Informal communications
- The hospital's "culture clarity"
- Physician support for hospital activities
- The level of respect that physicians have for the HIM staff

This book addresses the assessment process and steps you can take to identify specific issues and make improvements in the HIM–medical staff relationship.

THE ELECTRONIC MEDICAL RECORD AND CLINICAL DOCUMENTATION IMPROVEMENT

As healthcare organizations work toward implementing an electronic medical record (EMR), concerns about how clinical documentation is reflected in those records is growing. Some of the issues that need to be addressed include the compliant use of templates; getting physicians involved in the development of the EMR process itself (including procedures and the type of content to be collected); and the ability to integrate different components of the record and results to create an optimal record for each patient. This book addresses these issues as they relate to achieving high quality clinical documentation.

HOW TO USE THIS BOOK (VOLUMES 1 AND 2)

The information in this book is compiled from over 20 years of experience working with healthcare systems and performing research in clinical documentation practices and training. Over 500 hospitals and over 3,000 physicians have contributed in some way to the information presented in these volumes. In addition, among the organizations that contributed specifically to supporting the clinical documentation training study—the first of its kind—are the Hospital of the University of Pennsylvania; the Main Line Health System; the University of Maryland Medical System; St. Vincent's Medical Center in New York City; Navigant Consulting, Inc.; and HP3, Inc.

Volume 1 of this series provides a strategic approach to improving content of patient records through hospital–physician relationship development and training. Some may argue that clinical documentation is too operational to be included in a discussion on strategy. But Peter Drucker describes strategy as the means for converting "The Theory of the Business" into performance. In the case of healthcare, the patient record is the essence of the business. It is where all theory, practice, communication, thoughts, and activity converge. It is the common ground for everyone involved in the business of healthcare. Give it "the best care and feeding" and your business performance is likely to improve in terms of quality indicators; accuracy of reimbursement; reliability for legal and compliance purposes; planning and research; and, most importantly, increased healthcare consumer confidence and quality of care.

Volume 2 of this series provides the actual resources for assessments, training, and physician surveys. Using this information, you can replicate the studies that support the validity of the training put forth in these books. But more importantly, you can use these materials to deliver effective training to your physicians. This is *not* a turnkey solution. Every organization is different in terms of its approach and interaction with its employees and physicians. You will need to adapt the specific process to your needs. But as long as you apply the general methodology as described in volumes 1 and 2, you are certain to enjoy improved outcomes.

A NOTE ON CASE STUDIES

The case studies included in this book are based upon my experiences working with over 200 hospitals and healthcare systems that implemented clinical documentation programs. To preserve anonymity, I have omitted names and modified some inconsequential facts.

1. Development of the Four-step CAMP Method for Clinical Documentation Training

TRAINING is an essential component of implementing any new process, including a high quality clinical documentation program. Training is also important for continued sustainability of a program. Our team conducted a clinical documentation research study using scientific principles and an interventional design to test the effectiveness of the CAMP™ Method for training physicians to consistently produce high quality clinical documentation. The criteria used in the study, derived from official sources, defined high quality clinical documentation as documentation that is timely as well as legible, complete, reliable, clear, consistent, and precise.[1] The study found a positive relationship between the use of the CAMP Method for training and the likelihood of improving both physician clinical documentation quality and self-efficacy. The CAMP Method's foundation is the theory of self-efficacy, one of the most successful bases for adult learning. Self-efficacy training is used widely in school systems, the healthcare industry, government, and private industry. This chapter will explain the development of the CAMP Method for training. Chapters 2 through 6 explain implementation of the entire method as well as each component of the method.

The CAMP Method was developed over the course of 10 years through training programs provided to more than 3,000 physicians, conducted primarily at hospitals. The hospitals ranged in size from 25 to over 1,000 beds. They included community hospitals and academic medical centers, both for-profit and not-for-profit organizations. A team of physicians, nurse clinicians, health information management professionals, and PhD-level university-based instructors developed the testing instruments and guided the study process.

The specific design for testing the effectiveness of the CAMP Method for physician training was first conducted as a pilot study with residents and physicians at the Main Line Health family practice program in Radnor, Pennsylvania. After refining the study design using the results of the pilot, the final study was conducted with 91 internal medicine residents at the Hospital of the University of Pennsylvania, from February through April, 2007. The 91 participants were randomly assigned to one of three study groups:

- CAMP Method training group
- Limited training group
- Control group (no training)

Each group completed three questionnaires initially. Then the two training groups received training. The limited training group (LTG) received 90 minutes of training. The CAMP Method training group received four hours of training spread out over two training sessions with activities conducted in-between the training sessions. After the training was finished, each participant completed the same three questionnaires that he took at the beginning of the study. Questionnaires were anonymously coded so that a valid pre-and post-test analysis could be performed on the results. The three questionnaires covered:

- Physicians' confidence in their clinical documentation abilities (self-efficacy measure)
- A clinical documentation test
- Physicians' attitudes and opinions about clinical documentation

HOW SELF-EFFICACY AND TRAINING IMPACT QUALITY OF CLINICAL DOCUMENTATION

Every individual requires both knowledge and self-efficacy to successfully perform any task.[2] In fact, self-efficacy has been shown to be a better predictor of work-related performance than traditional

Figure 1.1. The Relationship Between Physician Input and Self-Efficacy and Training

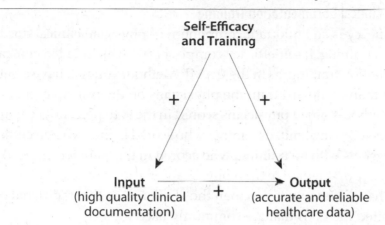

workplace attitudes, personality traits, the level of education, training and skill, goal setting, and feedback.[3] Every organization has an interest in increasing quality and overall organizational performance. Therefore, the use of self-efficacy based interventions to improve performance, as demonstrated through the CAMP Method study, may have implications for all organizations. In healthcare specifically, the clinical documentation input from the physician impacts an organization's output in terms of quality of care, quality indicators, reimbursement, and data for planning and research. The relationship between physician input, healthcare system output, and training and self-efficacy is illustrated in figure 1.1.

THREE MAJOR RESEARCH QUESTIONS

The research study was designed to answer three questions: First, if training alone would improve performance, does simultaneous improvement in self-efficacy enhance performance more than the training alone would have? Second, is performance likely to be better when training incorporates all four constructs of self-efficacy—the CAMP Method—as opposed to limited training? And third, does limited training improve self-efficacy or performance? Using these three research questions to guide the process, statistical analysis from the research study demonstrated two key points:

1. The CAMP Method Produces Superior Results in Physician Clinical Documentation Training

Self-efficacy is an important component of physician clinical documentation training. If self-efficacy components are included in clinical documentation training, as in the CAMP Method, you will have a better result than if you just train the physicians on the principles alone. CAMP Method-trained physicians scored in the 90th percentile versus physicians receiving limited training, who scored in the 80th percentile, and physicians with no training, who scored in the 60th percentile. By using the CAMP Method to train physicians in clinical documentation, you will have better outcomes than those offered by the traditional or more limited methods that are commonly used today.

2. CAMP Method Training Uses Self-Efficacy to Increase the Likelihood of the Sustainability of Training

While 90-minute limited training in clinical documentation produced some improvement, the improvement does not appear to be sustainable; and the degree of improvement is less than ideal, with physicians achieving test scores in the 80th percentile. Because the CAMP Method incorporates the four elements of self-efficacy, the training is more likely to be sustainable in the long term.

THE FIVE W'S OF THE CAMP METHOD STUDY FOR HIGH QUALITY CLINICAL DOCUMENTATION

This section addresses the rationale for the who, what, where, when, and why of the CAMP Method clinical documentation study.

Why?

Before beginning any study or endeavor, there really has to be a strong and valid reason for pursuing the activity. The "why" of any scientific research study is driven by previous research published in peer reviewed journals. In the business of healthcare, budgeting and spending are based on documentation provided by physicians for the care they provide to patients. Moreover, poor quality documentation in a patient's record has been linked to both excessive healthcare costs and poor quality of care.[4] The CAMP Method study applied self-efficacy theory, through an interventional study, to improve the clinical documentation of resident physicians in patient hospital records. This original application of self-efficacy theory is significant for its impact on decreasing healthcare costs, improving patient quality of care, and increasing efficiencies in healthcare.

Figure 1.2 identifies the research studies in peer reviewed literature that address the impact of self-efficacy and training for physicians and other clinicians. Two types of studies dominate the literature on the self-efficacy of clinicians. These are assessment or survey-based research, and training intervention, with a pre- and postintervention test. Fourteen of 26 studies used an educational session coupled with a pre- and postsession assessment to test self-efficacy improvement, similar to the study that the CAMP Method researchers conducted. Three of these studies were structured around pre-existing educational programs, including nursing or medical school students' clinical rotations. The training in these cases was not structured specifically around the self-efficacy constructs. Three of the interventional research studies were focused on testing the self-efficacy of resident physicians. The majority of the interventional studies were focused on physicians, and medical and nursing school students. The mean number of participants in the experimental groups for the interventional studies was 40. The range was 146, with a low of 10 experimental group participants and a high of 156 experimental group participants. The mean number of participants in the control groups for the interventional studies was 35. The range is 31, with a high of 46 and a low of 15 controls.

While there is a significant amount of literature related to the poor quality of clinical documentation in an inpatient medical record, the evolution of clinical documentation research is at the very early stages. The majority of the studies on lack of quality in clinical documentation have focused on identifying the problem without offering suggestions for improvement based on empirical findings. The CAMP Method study, however, successfully applied a training methodology and showed, through regression analysis modeling, significant improvement in the documentation practices of physicians involved in the study.

Figure 1.2. Summary of Self-Efficacy Studies Involving Clinicians

Researcher(s)	Study Type	Subjects	No. of Participants	Focus of the Study	M	P	C	A
Bravata, 2003	EPP	Residents	43 E; 37 CG	Self-directed learning skills				
Cabana et al., 2004	SAS	Physicians	457	Counseling: smoking cessation	■			
Carson & Gillham, 2005	EPP	Physicians	156 E; 40 CG	Counseling: cardiovascular		■		
Cheng et al., 1999	SAS	Physicians	556	Counseling: preventive care	■			
Chung et al., 2004	EPP	Physicians	17 E; 46 CG	Bioterrorism				
Engel et al., 1997	EPP	Medical students	41	Diabetic nutrition	■	■	■	■
Ford-Gilboe & Laschinger, 1997	EPP	Nursing students	30 E; 33 CG	Student competency	■	■	■	■
Gans et al., 1993	EPP	Residents	36 E	Cholesterol screening	■	■	■	■
Goldenberg, Andrusyszn & Iwasiw, 2005	EPP	Nursing students	22 E	Student competency	■	■	■	■
Gramling	SAS	Physicians	300	Cancer screening				
Katz, 2005	EPP	Physicians	17 E	Counseling obesity				
Coffman, Shellman & Bernal, 2004	SAS	Nursing students	22 E	Caring for African-American patients	■	■		
Laschinger & McWilliams, 1999	EPP	Medical students	71 E	Counseling: health promotion	■	■	■	■
Lenzi, 2005	EPP	Residents	17 E	Communicating cancer treatment	■	■	■	■
Makni et al., 2002	SAS	Physicians		Smoking cessation	■	■	■	■
Mann, 1997	EPP	Physicians	17 E; 15 CG	Cholesterol-lowering practices	■	■	■	■
Mann, 2005	EPP	Medical students	83 E	Cholesterol-lowering practices	■	■	■	■

Researcher(s)	Study Type	Subjects	No. of Participants	Focus of the Study	M	P	C	A
Martin, 2005	EPP	Physicians	15 E	Communicating / breast cancer patients	∎	∎	∎	∎
Mavis, 2001	SAS	Medical students	82	Exam performance	∎			
Opacic, 2003	SAS	PA students	290	Competency	∎			
Reich, Bickman & Feflinger, 2004	EPP	Caregivers		Mental health services availability	∎	∎	∎	∎
Silverstein et al., 2003	SI	Physicians	472	Head start	∎			
Sommers, Muller & Chu, 2003	SAS	Medical students	10 E	Student competency	∎			
Thompson, 1993	SAS	Nursing students		Core competencies	∎			
Treolar, 2001	SAS	Residents	18	Emergency medicine	∎			
Zapka et al., 1999	SAS	Physicians	171	Smoking cessation	∎			

Key: EPP = Educational program with pre- and post-test; SAS = self-assessment survey; SI = structured interview; E = experimental group; CG = control group; M = Mastering; P= Peer learning; C = Coaching; A = Asking

The results of previous clinical documentation research were used in the CAMP Method study to ensure that any experiences or characteristics of residents shown to impact the quality of clinical documentation were included in the demographic questionnaire. More importantly, this study addresses several gaps in clinical documentation research. First, this is the first study to use the full set of official and "quasi-official" guidelines that define quality clinical documentation. Second, this study uses a self-efficacy based educational program that has not been previously applied. Third, while a few previous studies have focused on the quality of clinical documentation, none has clearly correlated clinical documentation self-efficacy experiences with the quality of clinical documentation. Fourth, previous studies have focused on the practicing physician's specialty (for example, orthopedic surgeons, cardiologists), and not on residents in training. This study focused on internal medicine residents for the possibility of generalizing results across the entire population of primary care physicians. The current research available on clinical documentation reveals that lack of adequate documentation is a major problem throughout the industry.[5] Figure 1.3 offers a brief synopsis of the current literature published on clinical documentation.

Who?

A study requires significant expenditures of time, money, and resources. In this case, several organizations were involved and the resources of many supporting organizations were used to design and conduct the study. First, the Hospital of the University of Pennsylvania medicine residents and Dr. Barry Fuchs gave their time and efforts to the study because they felt that achieving high quality clinical documentation was a worthy cause. In addition, Touro University International, Main Line Health System, DJ Iber Publishing, the Medical University of South Carolina, St. Peter's College, HP3, Navigant Consulting, and Dr. Ian Diener, the physician instructor, all had some involvement in the pursuit of the goal to identify the best possible training mechanism to attaining high quality clinical documentation in patient records.

Of great importance is the study population, the individual participants in the study itself. This study used medicine residents as study participants. Residents were chosen to participate in the study—and not medical school students or physicians—because of the significant research findings for poor documentation by residents.[6] Research has shown that educational intervention can make a significant impact on residents; and since residents are the physicians of the future, this kind of intervention will greatly influence future practices.

Research studies that were focused on improving self-efficacy in residents have shown improved outcomes for the behavior being studied.[7] Low quality clinical documentation in inpatient records by resident physicians has been identified through many research studies.

Figure 1.3. Summary of Clinical Documentation Research

Researchers	Study Type	Participants	Study Topic	Number of Participants / Cases [patient records]
Cascio et al., 2005	Case study	Physicians	Compartment syndrome	30 cases
Larson, Wiggins & Goldfarb, 2004	Case study	Residents	Prescription writing	75 cases
Carroll et al., 2003	Case study	Residents	Patient weight and medications	432 cases
Spencer et al., 1999	Case study	Physicians	Current smoking status	50 cases
Manfield et al., 2001	Survey	Surgeons	Orthopedic office records	71 participants
Jacob, 2001	Survey	Physicians	General documentation	100 participants
Bachman, 2003	Case study	Physicians	History and physical	116 participants
Sabinis, 2003	Case study	Physicians	Vaccination status	352 cases
Stengel et al., 2004	Intervention	Physicians	Use of a handheld computer to document	80 patients
DeVon, 2004	Case study	Surgeons	Symptoms of acute MI	Not available
Flynn, 2004	Case study	Physicians and residents	Operative notes	550 cases
Marco & Buchman, 2003	Intervention	Surgeons	Orthopedic surgeons	181 cases
Mulvehill, 2005	Intervention	Physicians	Structured clinic notes	1339 cases
Weitzel, 2001	Case study	Physicians	Use of a checklist	43 cases
Socolar, 1998	Survey	Physicians	Child sexual abuse	72 exp; 75 controls
Humphreys, 1992	Intervention	Physicians	Emergency department	Not available
Novitsky, 2005	Case study	Residents	Operative reports	Not available
Elizondo, 1985	Survey	Residents	Operative reports	236 participants
Shaughnessy & D'Amico, 1994	Intervention	Residents	Prescription writing	Not available

Moreover, few interventional studies have been undertaken to improve clinical documentation. The CAMP Method researchers were unable to locate any studies that examined the effectiveness of an educational program designed to improve the self-efficacy of internal medicine resident physicians regarding their general clinical documentation skills. Studies on the relationship between self-efficacy and clinical documentation have been very focused on specific documentation practices, which limits the impact of findings in these cases.

The population from which the sample was drawn consisted of resident physicians from the internal medicine residency program at the Hospital of the University of Pennsylvania. All residents who participated in the study were: (1) internal medicine residents, or currently in their internal medicine rotation within their residency programs; (2) first, second, third, or fourth year residents; (3) not exposed to previous clinical documentation training; and (4) practicing in the same hospital system. These sample selection criteria were utilized to create a higher probability that the study participants were similar and would, therefore, decrease the likelihood of confounders being introduced into the data.

Healthcare providers generally have been identified to have poor quality documentation practices.[8] Resident physicians, in particular, have been identified in many studies with particularly significant documentation problems. One study reported an 80 percent error rate in resident documentation for patient surgical procedures.[9] A second study found that of the bills generated based on resident dictation of operative procedures, 28 percent were inaccurate.[10] A third study found resident documentation errors in the neonatal intensive care unit as high as 67 percent.[11] A fourth study found that resident documentation was inadequate in 70 percent of the patient cases reviewed. This included 53 percent of the cases where documentation was illegible.[12]

Since residents are the physicians of the future, these findings are particularly alarming. It has been suggested that a likely reason for the widespread lack of proper documentation is a lack of emphasis on careful documentation in medical school and residency. The Accreditation Council for Graduate Medical Education (ACGME) recently implemented six general core curriculum competencies: patient care, medical knowledge, practice-based learning and improvement, interpersonal and communication skills, professionalism, and systems-based practice. The Council, responsible for accrediting the 7,000 residency training programs, has stated that residency programs must require their residents to achieve these competencies in order to become effective practitioners. As trainees, resident physicians are strongly influenced by the behavior and practices of their faculty role-models. In addition, they develop the confidence to practice medicine independently through a series of patient care assignments in which they are given increasing levels of autonomy. Thus, developing a strong sense of confidence in one's abilities is essential for achieving clinical competence.

These statements from the ACGME regarding residents' confidence and the need for role models are helpful in defining the movement of the profession to becoming more results-oriented in the six competencies defined by the organization. However, self-efficacy involves more than confidence in one's own abilities generally. Self-efficacy involves an individual's assessment of his own capabilities in (1) being motivated, (2) garnering necessary resources, and (3) taking action in regard to a specific task. Physicians are not likely to take independent action to improve their clinical documentation. The CAMP Method study findings can reverse this trend and create a positive and significant impact on healthcare organizations.

What?

Here we address *what* was done to improve the problem of poor quality documentation. Specifically, a research study was designed and conducted to test the CAMP Method for improving physician clinical documentation. The research design utilized in this study was a quasi-experimental pre- and post-test design. The study investigated the relationship between a specific clinical documentation educational intervention, resident physician self-efficacy, and clinical documentation quality. The literature on self-efficacy and research shows that the next logical step in testing possible solutions for the problem should be through the use of an interventional educational program accompanied by pre- and post-test assessments from the participants.

The study participants were assigned to one of three groups: the control group, the CAMP Method training group, or the limited training group. Each study group was exposed to a different educational intervention. The CAMP Method training group was exposed to all four components of self-efficacy: *coaching, asking, mastering,* and *peer learning.* The limited training group was exposed to only two components of self-efficacy, *coaching* and *asking.* The limited training group did not have the opportunity to participate in or master clinical documentation improvement activities during their training, whereas the CAMP Method training group was involved in applying the concepts they learned. The control group received no educational intervention during the study period. All groups attended two sessions, approximately 7 to 10 days apart. Prior to any intervention, all groups completed three questionnaires: (1) a self-efficacy assessment, (2) a clinical documentation test, and (3) a demographic questionnaire. These questionnaires are contained in the appendix. During the second session, all participants completed a second self-efficacy assessment and clinical documentation test.

Where?

The study was conducted at a well-known academic medical center for several reasons. First, to attain statistical significance, it was necessary to have a minimum of 91 residents participate in the study. Residents were preferred to be from the same specialty, in this case internal medicine, and from the same hospital so as not to produce significant confounders. Therefore, it was necessary to find an academic medical center both interested in the improvement of clinical documentation and large enough to meet the study needs. In addition, it was essential that the academic medical center did not already have an established clinical documentation education program in place for residents. The resident participants in the study needed to be new to a hospital-based clinical documentation training program. The medicine residency program of the Hospital of the University of Pennsylvania met these criteria. Furthermore, the study needed to be approved by the university's Institutional Review Board (IRB) and the study investigators needed to participate in mandatory University of Pennsylvania IRB training. These activities ensured high academic and scientific rigor in the study process.

When?

The pilot study at Main Line Health System was conducted during the fourth quarter of 2006 and the clinical documentation study at the Hospital of the University of Pennsylvania was conducted during the first and second quarters of 2007. The timing for the study was concurrent with the federal government's decision to begin using a severity-based reimbursement system for Medicare hospital inpatient cases. Since a severity system relies even more on accurate clinical documentation than the previous resource-based diagnostic related groups (DRG) system for Medicare hospital inpatient cases, increased interest in high quality clinical documentation was generated.

HOW THE STUDY WAS PERFORMED

In addition to the Five W's of the program, it is essential to understand how the study was performed. This chapter provides an overview of the study procedures. Chapters 2 through 6 provide more detail on each specific component of the study.

First, let's look at the three instruments used to collect data for the study, namely, the self-efficacy questionnaire, the clinical documentation test, and the attitudes and opinions questionnaire.

Self-Efficacy Questionnaire and Validation

The self-efficacy questionnaire asked the participants to rate the quality of their clinical documentation and then to rate how confident they were that they could document certain pieces of clinical information in a patient's medical record. There were 22 total questions included in the questionnaire. Because there has been no specific research on self-efficacy related to inpatient clinical documentation practices, there is currently no complete questionnaire already developed on the topic. Therefore, to ensure the highest possible degree of reliability and validity, formats and components of surveys from validated instruments used in previous research were adapted for the CAMP study. In addition, the instrument was pilot tested and validated by one group of residents before finalizing the main instrument.

Twenty-two physicians completed the survey instrument during the pilot. A Cronbach's alpha was performed on the survey instrument using pilot survey data. This analysis yielded a coefficient of .872. The details of this analysis can be found in figure 1.4. Cronbach's alpha measures how well a set of items measures a single unidimensional latent construct. When data have a multidimensional structure, Cronbach's alpha will usually be low. Generally, if the inter-item correlations are high, then there is evidence that the items are measuring the same underlying construct. A reliability coefficient of .70 or higher is considered "acceptable" in most research situations. Because the coefficient for this instrument was .872, it is safe to assume that the items are measuring the same underlying construct.

A factor analysis was also performed on the same set of 22 pilot survey instruments to ensure that the items included on the instrument were homogenous. A factor analysis attempts to identify underlying variables that explain the pattern of correlations within a set of observed variables. The factor analysis results indicate the amount of variance accounted for in each variable. Small values, or an extraction value of less than .6, indicate variables that do not fit well within the solution and should possibly be dropped from the analysis. The factor analysis performed on the self-efficacy instrument showed no values less than .6. In fact, the range for the 24 questionnaire values was .619 to .874, with a mean of .7308. Therefore, all questionnaire variables were kept intact for the statistical analysis of this study.

The questionnaire uses the same question format and item scales used by many of the self-efficacy research studies identified in this literature review. Each question in the self-efficacy survey used in this study begins with the statement "I am confident that I can . . ." This is the exact format used by the self-efficacy questionnaires in the Katz and Cabana studies. In addition, the survey uses the same Likert scale, 0 to 4, corresponding to *Not at all, A little, Somewhat, Mostly,* and *Completely,* used in the Lenz and Shortridge-Bagett study (figure 1.7). In addition, the self-efficacy questionnaire used in this research is similar to the

Figure 1.4. Results of Cronbach's Alpha Analysis on Self-Efficacy Questionnaire

Cronbach's Alpha	Cronbach's Alpha Based on Standardized Items	Number of Items
.872	.886	24

Figure 1.5. Cronbach's Alpha Item Statistics

Questionnaire Item	Mean	Standard Deviation
Legibility	3.23	.735
H&P	3.57	.542
H&P 24	3.84	.364
Chronic Conditions	3.12	.615
Acute Conditions	3.50	.525
Abnormal Diagnostic Tests	3.03	.550
Radiology Reports	3.21	.679
Path Report	3.17	.675
Progress Notes	3.36	.624
Discharge Summary	2.38	1.097
Etiology: Chest Pain	3.41	.538
Etiology: Abdominal Pain	3.11	.589
Etiology: Shortness of Breath	3.32	.577
Etiology: Syncope	2.99	.727
Etiology: Vertigo	2.59	.685
Abnormal: Lab Test	3.21	.486
Abnormal: EKG	2.99	.551
Abnormal: X-ray	3.11	.507
Abnormal: CT Scan	3.04	.517
Abnormal: Culture & Sensitivity	3.29	.640
Abnormal: Echocardiogram	3.13	.603
Code Accurate Diagnoses	2.36	.798
Medicare Documentation Requirements	2.09	.967
JCAHO Documentation Requirements	2.09	.856

structured questionnaire recommended by Bandura.

Finally, the results of the pilot test, discussed below, were utilized to refine the survey instrument and ensure a sufficient level of statistical reliability. Content validation of the tools was established by a panel of physician, nursing, and clinical documentation experts to determine whether each item on the tool assesses self-efficacy related to clinical documentation. The panel was composed of four physicians, one nurse, and one clinical documentation expert. The complete questionnaire is included in the appendix.

Pre-test and Post-test

The same test was administered to study participants before and after training. The content of the clinical documentation test was reviewed, modified, and approved by the same expert panel that reviewed the self-efficacy questionnaire. The clinical documentation test completed by the participants was composed of two sections: (1) a multiple choice section addressing basic knowledge of clinical documentation requirements and regulations, and (2) a written response section where residents were asked to document patient diagnoses based on clinical information provided in case study type questions. The clinical documentation test content included examples of guidelines identified by official sources as documentation that is timely, legible, complete, clear, consistent, reliable, and precise. There were 15 total questions included in the questionnaire. Each question addresses at least one of the characteristics of clinical documentation. The specific documentation characteristic being tested by each question is included on the answer key for the pre-test and post-test document.

In addition to correct responses, the answer key for the test also contains the number of points to be assigned for each correct answer or portion of an answer. For example, the correct response to question B in part two of the document is "acute blood loss anemia." The total number of points for the correct response is five. However, if the physician documents some portion of the diagnosis correctly, he will receive partial credit. Broken down into its components, each term or phrase in the correct response will receive the following points: *acute* =

Figure 1.6. Extraction Values for Factor Analysis of Self-Efficacy Questionnaire

Questionnaire variable	Initial	Extraction
Legibility	1.000	.874
H&P	1.000	.749
H&P 24	1.000	.723
Chronic Conditions	1.000	.708
Acute Conditions	1.000	.619
Abnormal Diagnostic Tests	1.000	.772
Radiology Reports	1.000	.792
Path Report	1.000	.760
Progress Notes	1.000	.653
Discharge Summary	1.000	.802
Etiology: Chest Pain	1.000	.825
Etiology: Abdominal Pain	1.000	.780
Etiology: Shortness of Breath	1.000	.774
Etiology: Syncope	1.000	.791
Etiology: Vertigo	1.000	.790
Abnormal: Lab Test	1.000	.766
Abnormal: EKG	1.000	.700
Abnormal: X-ray	1.000	.698
Abnormal: CT Scan	1.000	.786
Abnormal: Culture & Sensitivity	1.000	.777
Abnormal: Echocardiogram	1.000	.738
Code Accurate Diagnoses	1.000	.754
Medicare Documentation Requirements	1.000	.852
JCAHO Documentation Requirements	1.000	.859

Figure 1.7. Likert Scale Used in Self-Efficacy Questionnaire

Not at all	A little	Somewhat	Mostly	Completely
0	1	2	3	4

1; *blood loss* = 2; *anemia* = 1. In addition, the participant received an additional point if the documentation was deemed legible by a physician member of the test development group. This concept of peer review for legibility is derived from the Sinai Hospital legibility program. In this program, physician documentation is periodically reviewed for legibility. A physician-peer reviews the documentation, and, if she is able to read the documentation, the documentation passes the legibility test. However, if the physician is not able to read the documentation, then the documentation fails, and the physician author is required to successfully complete a course on legibility.

Each test was scored by dividing the number of correct points by the total number of points on the test, which is 73 total points. The result is a percentage from 0 percent to 100 percent, assigned to each pre-test and each post-test. Each participant, then, received three scores for both the pre-test and the post-test: (1) a score for the multiple choice section of the pre-test from 0 percent to 100 percent, (2) a score for the written section of the exam from 0 percent to 100 percent, and (3) a score for the overall test, to include both the multiple choice and the written sections of the test, from 0 percent to 100 percent. Since it is more valuable to utilize the data at the most specific level, individual scores were used for the initial regression models. In addition to calculating one score for each test, separate scores for each characteristic of clinical documentation—with the exception of timeliness, which cannot be calculated in this manner—were calculated. The questions themselves are identified as testing one or more of the characteristics of high quality clinical documentation. As a result, in addition to a total score for the overall test, each participant was assigned six "sub-scores"—one for each documentation characteristic.

The clinical documentation test was pilot tested by two groups of physicians prior to being used. First, the panel of four physician experts who recommended modifications to the test, completed the test initially. Second, a group of 22 residents started and 14 residents completed the pilot study. The residents were from a family practice residency program in suburban Philadelphia. These residents took the test as part of the pilot study. Feedback from the test-takers resulted in

Figure 1.8. Components of Good Clinical Documentation Practices

Important considerations	Document ...	Examples: if present or *suspected* document ...
Patient's principal diagnosis	Detail, precision	*"Aspiration"* pneumonia; *"acute"* renal failure; cerebral *"infarct"*
Chronic diagnoses	Every diagnosis	COPD, CHF, seizures, pulmonary fibrosis
Acute co-existing diagnoses	Every diagnosis treated	Malnutrition, respiratory failure, dehydration
Abnormal diagnostic tests	Clinical significance of the result	Hyponatremia; mitral regurgitation; atrial fibrillation
Symptoms	Etiology or "suspected" cause of the symptom	Instead of chest pain ... possible GERD; angina due to CAD; instead of syncope ... arrhythmia (all only if clinically supported)

some minor modifications to the testing instrument. First, the verbal and written directions were modified to provide more clarification and focus to the test-takers. Second, the ordering of the multiple choice and written sections of the test were changed. Finally, a few words used in a question about ordering Lasix for a patient with congestive heart failure were changed to ensure the clarity of the question. The complete questionnaire is included in the appendix. Figure 1.8 illustrates the specific clinical documentation components that residents were tested and instructed on

As noted above, the test includes objective, multiple choice questions and also requires written responses. The written responses tested actual practices as well as legibility. The questions on the test correspond directly to the objectives of the educational interventional program. The responses were reviewed and corrected using the answer key and converted to data for statistical analysis via a percentage grading system. Each question was assigned a numeric value based upon the importance of the construct in the overall concept of clinical documentation quality. The total points obtained were divided by total points in the test to obtain an overall percentage score for each participant.

Attitudes and Opinions Questionnaire

The purpose of the attitudes and opinions questionnaire was two-fold. First, the questionnaire collected basic information about each participant. Second, and more importantly, the information collected via the demographic questionnaire included potential control variable information. The demographic questionnaire asked the participants certain questions about their background and investigated their attitudes and opinions about, and experiences with, clinical documentation. Thirteen questions were included on the demographic questionnaire and the questionnaire was administered primarily for informational purposes. However, in every self-efficacy study it is important to collect information about the individual participant's perceptions of knowledge, skills, and resources. This study collected both objective and perceptual data. One key data element collected on this survey was the physician's own rating of the quality of his documentation. The physician was asked in the last question on the survey to rate the quality of his documentation using the following scale: *poor, fair, good, very good*, or *excellent*.

The attitudes and opinions questionnaire collected information on the physician's beliefs about her clinical documentation. In one set of questions, the physician is asked to rate on a scale of *not at all* to *a great deal* how she believes her documentation impacts the patient's quality of care, her medical malpractice exposure, report card ratings, Medicare quality indicators, and Joint Commission accreditation, among other things. This data was used to cross-tabulate some of the statistical analysis in both the documentation test and the self-efficacy questionnaire. This questionnaire is included in the appendix.

CHAPTER SUMMARY

The CAMP Method study was conducted in 2006–2007 to determine the viability of the method for ensuring improved documentation quality and improved self-efficacy of the physician trainees. The study found that the CAMP Method produces superior results in both physician clinical documentation quality and self-efficacy. The method used four components, reflected in the acronym, to help ensure an effective and sustainable learning process. These training components are *coaching, asking, mastering,* and *peer learning.* The study was conducted using internal medicine residents at the Hospital of the University of Pennsylvania.

STEPS YOU CAN TAKE TODAY

- Share the study description with physicians on your staff who have a particular interest in research.
- Speak with other managers about the possibility of training a small group of your physicians using the CAMP Method for clinical documentation training.
- Ask a few physicians to complete one of the survey instruments and review the results with them, offering or receiving feedback about how they completed the test, survey, or questionnaire.

2. The CAMP Method Components for Clinical Documentation Training

HIGH QUALITY clinical documentation is defined as documentation that is timely, legible, complete, reliable, clear, consistent (unambiguous), and precise. The CAMP™ Method is a training process that uses four main training components or methodologies to develop self-efficacy. These training components are:

- *Coaching*, which involves coaching and encouraging participants about their abilities to perform this function.
- *Asking*, which involves soliciting feedback from the physician participants in a specific manner and at a specific time.
- *Mastering*, which involves practical application of the principles demonstrated and discussed during the training program.
- *Peer Learning*, which involves instruction by a knowledgeable peer, someone who has participated in the activity of high quality clinical documentation and can demonstrate that to the learner.

Key guidelines and regulations from the Medicare Conditions of Participation and the Joint Commission address the requirements for a physician to "document the clinical significance of every abnormal test result," "to document a complete history and physical," "the etiology or possible etiology of symptoms," and "daily progress notes." To stress the importance of clinical documentation, the program content also includes instruction in the Official Guidelines for Coding and Reporting and the Uniform Hospital Discharge Data Set (UHDDS), published by the Centers for Disease Control. In addition, the instructors discussed the basic steps for translating the physician's documentation into coded data by using the ICD-9-CM and Current Procedural Terminology (CPT) disease and procedure classification systems. Participants were informed that after the documentation in a patient's record has been translated into coded data, these data are used as the basis for billing, quality of care analysis, healthcare research, and planning. Medicare Conditions of Participation (COPs) describe the documentation requirements for patients whose health insurance is provided by a federal government entity (Medicare, Medicaid, Tri-care). The Joint Commission's documentation guidelines apply to any organizations seeking accreditation or already accredited by the Joint Commission. Because the UHDDS and the Official Guidelines for Coding and Reporting are the only guidelines that apply equally across all healthcare providers, they were given precedence in this study. In many instances, the Medicare COPs and the Joint Commission's guidelines provide more detailed information for clinical documentation. As a result, these requirements were used as secondary sources for defining the quality of clinical documentation.

Each year, the Federal Bureau of Investigation and the Department of Health and Human Services' Office of Inspector General investigate and prosecute healthcare providers who show patterns of inaccurate Medicare billing for services not supported by clinical documentation in the patient's record. The Department of Health and Human Services has estimated that healthcare providers overbill the Medicare program approximately 40 billion dollars per year. Twelve billion dollars of over-billing annually, or roughly one-third of the total amount, is attributed to inaccurate, incomplete, or ambiguous clinical documentation by physicians in patient records.

The CAMP Method study utilized a three-group pre- and post-educational intervention design to study the effects of two different educational programs against a control group that did not receive any education. The study methodology is illustrated in the figure 2.1.

The clinical documentation educational intervention consisted of either two 2-hour sessions or one 90-minute session provided to the

Figure 2.1. CAMP Method Study Methodology

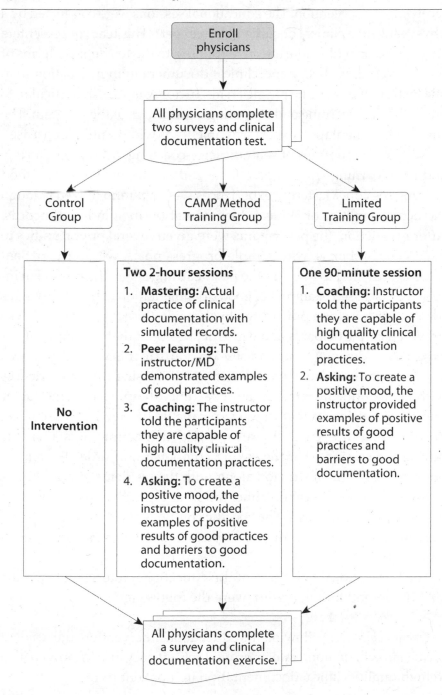

resident physician participants in the study group. The control group received no intervention. The educational sessions were conducted by a physician and a clinical documentation expert. This team of presenters was able to provide more effective training to the residents in terms of both self-efficacy theory and clinical documentation instruction than one instructor alone. The physician instructor was able, in particular, to guide the peer learning and mastering experiences of the program. The clinical documentation expert was able to provide content expertise.

All four foundations of self-efficacy—coaching, asking, mastering, and peer learning—were operationalized during the CAMP Method training session. Mastering experiences were operationalized through the actual practice of clinical documentation in simulated records. After instruction, the participants were given several opportunities to document problems, with sample progress notes, within the patient records provided to them. In the peer learning stage, the physician instructor discussed examples of good documentation habits through his own experiences as a practicing physician. In this stage, feedback was provided by participants to the instructors about their documentation experiences during the second session. Participants were also shown a seven-minute video clip of physicians discussing their experiences with clinical documentation. For coaching, the physician instructor told the participants that they were capable of high quality clinical documentation practices. He also provided encouraging statements during the sessions. For the asking component, in order to create a positive mood, the instructor, along with the residents, discussed the barriers to good clinical documentation and positive results of good documentation practices. The specific components of the training sessions are described for your own implementation purposes in chapters 3 through 6.

The instructional objectives of the educational intervention for the CAMP Method training group were the following:

Overall objective: Following the educational intervention, the resident physician will demonstrate improved self-efficacy and improved skill in high quality clinical documentation in inpatient records.

Figure 2.2. Variable Labels

Acronym	Translation	Role
PCDQ	Preintervention clinical documentation quality	IV
CDQ	Clinical documentation quality (postintervention)	DV
PCDSE	Preintervention clinical documentation self-efficacy rating	IV
CDSE	Clinical documentation self-efficacy rating (postintervention)	DV, moderator
CAMP	Subject was a member of the CAMP Method training group	IV/dummy
LTG	Subject was a member of the Limited Training group	IV/dummy

Specific objectives: The resident physician will:

1. Demonstrate understanding of the relationship between physician documentation and the translation of that documentation into ICD-9-CM coded data.
2. Demonstrate an understanding that ICD-9-CM coded data is used for planning, reimbursement, quality ratings, Medicare Conditions of Participation, Joint Commission Core Measures, and research.
3. Provide documentation in the inpatient record that is timely, legible, complete, clear, consistent, reliable, and precise.
4. Document detail and precision in the patient's principal diagnosis.
5. Document all chronic coexisting secondary diagnoses.
6. Document all acute coexisting secondary diagnoses.
7. Document the clinical significance of all abnormal diagnostic tests.
8. Document the etiology or suspected etiology of symptoms.

DEPENDENT VARIABLES: CLINICAL DOCUMENTATION QUALITY (CDQ) AND CLINICAL DOCUMENTATION SELF-EFFICACY (CDSE)

The study was designed around two dependent variables. Depending on what was being measured, the dependent variable was either clinical documentation quality (CDQ) or clinical documentation self-efficacy (CDSE). CDQ was measured through the difference between each participant's clinical documentation pre- and postintervention test scores. CDSE was measured through the difference between each participant's clinical documentation pre- and postintervention questionnaire scores.

EDUCATIONAL INTERVENTIONAL PROGRAMS

The programs were conducted by a physician with clinical documentation expertise and a clinical documentation expert. The programs were preplanned and scripted for content consistent with either the two or four elements of self-efficacy training, depending on the program. Both programs contained the same substantive content. The primary difference between the CAMP Method training program and the limited training program was the format for the delivery of the information and instruction. The CAMP Method program was comprised of two 2-hour sessions. The limited training program was one 90-minute session. The study secondarily sought to determine whether performance would suffer if training programs were shortened (as they usually are) to not include the mastering and peer learning stages. The regression models showed that performance would suffer in this case.

Consistent with prior research in training and self-efficacy, this study intended to increase the physician's awareness and knowledge of the subject by providing study participants with tools. Physician participants were given a copy of the *Clinical Documentation Improvement Handbook for Physicians* by Navigant Consulting and pocket cards with tips for good documentation.

The educational session utilized in this research: (1) provided accurate descriptions of the tasks to be performed; (2) instructed participants about the best means to perform the task; (3) eliminated physical distractions; (4) did not focus on training new skills, but rather focused on enhancing the participants' beliefs about what they could do with the skills they already had; (5) implemented the training close in time to the task they needed to perform (clinical documentation); (6) provided clear and objective standards against which the participants gauged the level of their performance accomplishment; and (7) attached consequences to the participant's performance of the task.[1]

Figure 2.3. Training Recommendations

#	Training recommendations from the Stajkovic and Luthans study
1	Provide accurate descriptions of the tasks participants are asked to perform.
2	Instruct participants about the best means to perform the task and technology.
3	Eliminate physical distractions.
4	Do not focus on training participants on new skills. Do focus on enhancing the participants' beliefs about what they can do with the skills they already have.
5	Implement the efficacy enhancement program close in time to the task the participants are asked to perform.
6	Provide clear and objective standards for participants to gauge the level of their performance accomplishment.
7	Contingently attach consequences to the participant's performance of the task.

Figure 2.4. Educational Activities Performed During CAMP Method Training for Physicians

Concept	Application
Peer Learning	1. Showed video of physicians discussing documentation issues and solutions to those issues. 2. Shared examples of good documentation by physicians in patient records. 3. Co-participants in the study provided an example of how they would document accurately and correctly. 4. Physician conducting the session provided examples of how to document accurately and correctly. 5. Examples were shared of how the information learned in the first session was applied by members of the study group.
Mastering	1. Each participant had the opportunity to accurately and correctly document diagnoses in the five problem areas from sample medical record information. 2. Tools were provided to each participant to use while documenting. These included a handbook and cue cards for reference.
Coaching	1. Instructor pointed out that the information that needs to be documented is "in the physician's head"; they just needed to learn to translate it to the written word. 2. Discussed the importance of complete and accurate documentation to the patient. 3. Discussed the job of the "translators" of the physicians' documentation and how they needed the physician's complete documentation to do their job. 4. Feedback was provided during each session based on how well the participants did in their pre-test and their participation in class exercises.
Asking	1. Dinner was provided at each session. 2. Discussed the frustrations physicians have with complying with increasing regulations in healthcare. 3. Discussed the monetary impact of incomplete or inaccurate documentation. 4. Discussed the quality of care impact of incomplete or inaccurate documentation. 5. Discussed time management issues.

As an incentive to complete the entire training program, residents who completed all requirements of the study were paid $120 per hour for their time. This amount was slightly higher than the current per diem rates for residents. In conjunction with the medical director of the academic medical center, the researchers determined that by paying the residents a higher hourly amount than what they would receive for other, part-time work, they would be likely to participate and return to complete the study. In addition, the residents' participation in the sessions met competencies defined by the Accreditation Council for Graduate Medical Education (ACGME). Figure 2.4 provides a summary of the educational activities performed during each step of the CAMP Method training for physicians.

THE PILOT STUDY

A pilot study was conducted prior to the research study. The purpose of the pilot study was primarily to test and validate the instruments and the training intervention. The pilot study was conducted at the Main Line Health Center and Bryn Mawr Family Practice program in suburban Philadelphia. A total of 22 residents started and 14 residents completed the entire intervention. The study followed the exact procedures planned for the CAMP Method training study. First, the residents completed the three pre-test questionnaires. Then the physician instructor and the clinical documentation expert conducted a two-hour education session. The residents were asked to apply what they learned during the first session and return approximately one week later. When the residents returned, the physician instructor asked them to describe how they applied the concepts from the first session in their practice during the past week. At the end of the second training session, the residents completed the post-test and the postintervention self-efficacy questionnaire.

The following changes were made to the questionnaires and training program as a result of the pilot study. First, the instructions for completing the questionnaires were clarified and scripted to ensure that each group would hear the same, exact instructions. Second, the order in which the questionnaires were completed was changed so the self-efficacy questionnaire was completed first, the documentation test completed second, and the demographic questionnaire completed last. This was based upon feedback from the participants regarding the length of the demographic questionnaire. Third, the amount of time dedicated to the discussion about concerns and opportunity to apply the concepts learned was increased because not all participants in the pilot study were able to participate in the discussions at the time originally scheduled. Fourth, the methodology used to assign study numbers and handout questionnaires was refined. For example, instead of asking the participants to write their study number on the questionnaires, the research assistant performed this task. In addition, she wrote the identification numbers on each page of the questionnaires in the event that they became unfastened. Finally, based on participant feedback, we decided to spend less time on the re-review of concepts during the second session and added more time for the residents to spend reviewing sample records and identifying problematic documentation.

EDUCATIONAL PROGRAM EVALUATION

A brief program evaluation was administered to all participants at the completion of the program. The purpose of the postsession evaluation was to determine participant satisfaction with the program. The program evaluation contained both Likert-scale type items and open-ended questions. In addition, information collected from the participants during the postsession evaluation may be helpful in future program design. A copy of the postsession evaluation can be found in the appendix.

ETHICAL CONSIDERATIONS

The Hospital of the University of Pennsylvania's IRB application procedures required the instructors to successfully complete the medical center's IRB course before submitting the official application. This course was completed by the instructors in October 2006. Application was made to the IRB in November 2006 and approval was granted in late January 2007. The Medical Center's consent form was required to be used during the study process. When the residents arrived for the study, they were given a complete copy of the consent form and asked to read it during dinner and then sign it if they still wanted to participate. Giving the residents time over dinner to read the form ensured they had enough time to comprehend the information prior to signing. All residents who showed up for the study signed the consent form.

A system of assigning identification numbers to the residents after they signed in for the study session was used to ensure that confidentiality would be protected. The sign-in sheets with resident names and corresponding identification numbers were subsequently destroyed after all of the data was collected, input, and stored electronically. This process was explained to the residents at the beginning of the program. In addition, after data was collected from the participants, they were told that it would only be reported in an anonymous, aggregate manner to continue to protect their confidentiality.

Residents who were interested in participating in the study received an informational statement describing the study and their responsibilities. Residents were told that they would be paid for their participation after they completed the entire research process. The payment that the resident physicians received for participating was not tied to any subjective criteria. Rather, the participant received payment as long as he completed the entire study through to the post-test. To avoid any bias, the criteria for payment was the same for both the control and the study groups.

A final ethical consideration is the fact that control group members did not have the opportunity to improve their clinical documentation skills by attending the educational sessions. As a result, the control group received the same 90-minute training session as the limited study group during week two, *after* they had completed their post-test and second self-efficacy questionnaire.

DATA COLLECTION PROCEDURES

This section discusses data collection, data analysis, and the management of threats to internal validity. Data was collected from study participants via the use of three instruments. A clinical documentation self-efficacy questionnaire, a clinical documentation test, and a demographic questionnaire were administered prior to intervention and after intervention for the experimental groups, approximately one week apart. The same questionnaires were completed by control group participants approximately one week apart with no intervention during the interim period. The pre- and post-self-efficacy questionnaire and medical documentation test were administered to the control group approximately one week apart.

All three questionnaires were administered in person to all participants during the time slots set aside by the medical director and the residency program director for each group. As noted previously in the methodology section, the residents attended sessions based on their current rotation schedules. A total of 188 discrete data elements were collected for each study participant through the three instruments. Many of the elements were aggregated together to represent one variable in the study. For example, self-efficacy was measured through 25 data elements prior to the intervention and 25 data elements after the intervention. Each data element represented the participant's response to a question. The data elements were then aggregated together to represent three self-efficacy subscores and one self-efficacy score overall for the statistical analysis.

The researcher used a scripted outline to convey the directions consistently to each group. In addition, the questionnaires contained directions for completion. The research assistant remained in the room while the questionnaires were completed. Upon completion, the research assistant collected each questionnaire. At the time of collection, the research assistant scanned the questionnaires to ensure that, generally, all questions were answered. This process was used to decrease the likelihood of missing data elements.

Each test was corrected consistent with the key in the appendix. Test questions on the demographic questionnaire and the self-efficacy questionnaire that contained text responses were entered into a Microsoft Word file by participant identification number. Once the questionnaires were collected, tests were corrected, and all questionnaires were validated for content, they were entered into an SPSS version 14.0 database for analysis. The text files were analyzed using a Key Word in Context (KWIC) program.

THE MANAGEMENT OF THREATS TO INTERNAL VALIDITY

Could potential bias result from the fact that residents were paid to participate in the study? Claims that there might be something different, or confounding, about participants who volunteer to participate in a study where they will be paid, could be made. However, in this case, all residents were in the same position of being paid on customary scale, regardless of group. Since all participants received an honorarium, the argument that no bias would be introduced is the stronger one. In addition, the residents who did participate in the study represented over 90 percent of the internal medicine residents at the medical center. Therefore, a more than representative sampling of residents in this program was obtained.

Previous exposure to clinical documentation training could be a confounder. Prior clinical documentation training was listed as exclusion criteria in all of the recruitment brochures circulated to residents. Residents read the qualification criteria during the dinner just before the first session. They were also told verbally during the initial instructions that if they had participated in a similar training program previously, they could not participate in this study.

Possible limiting factors to the statistical relationships identified in this study include the similarity of the sample group and the location of the study. The sample group, by nature of their current status as internal medicine residents, were generally of similar age, educational background, and professional interests. While these similarities provide the basis for consistent findings, they may also be a confounder to other relationships identified in the study. The study addressed this in two ways. First, the findings cannot be generalized beyond the specific population that was the subject of this research. Second, the study used some of the demographic data collected during the process as control variables in the regression equation. These data may be helpful in explaining what may be perceived as confounders.

Another possible confounder could be the location of the study. There might be claims that since the study was conducted in a particular hospital and/or in a particular section of the country, that would impact the findings. But in identifying the location and the hospital,

Figure 2.5. Course Contents of the First Two-hour Educational Program for CAMP Method Training

Construct	Activity	Program Design to Foster Construct	Time
Peer learning, coaching, and asking	Introduction	Review session outline and objectives. Physician instructor shares own experience with clinical documentation and assures participants that, with the appropriate training and support, they will master this process.	10 min
Mastering	Self-assessment and test	Participants take the self-assessment and the pre-test. Collect the self-assessment and the pre-test from the participants before reviewing the responses.	10 min
Peer learning	Test review	Review test questions and correct responses with attendees.	10 min
Asking	Resident commitment to good clinical documentation	Discuss the relationship between good documentation practices and improved patient outcomes with the participants. Ask physicians to share their concerns about clinical documentation. Make a list of what they are and share the list (as a way to end this portion of the session). State that we will revisit the list in the second session. Include time management if not addressed by physicians.	10 min
Peer learning	Documentation rules	Review documentation "rules" PowerPoint with physicians. Ask for and allow questions throughout this portion of the presentation.	15 min
Asking	Break	Serve refreshments and take a 5-minute break.	10 min
Mastering	Case study examples	Review cases studies 1–5 that correspond with objectives 2–5.	15 min
Mastering	Tools	Provide each physician with Navigant Consulting's *Clinical Documentation Improvement Handbook for Physicians* and a *Doc Pocket Tool*. Review the contents of the *Handbook* and the *Tool*. Allow for questions throughout this portion of the presentation.	15 min
Mastering and coaching	Case study exercises	Give physicians case study exercises 1–5 that contain documentation from actual patient records to review and provide the correct documentation to identify the patient's diagnosis/es. Review answers with physicians asking participants for their responses. Provide feedback as each participant shares her answers.	15 min
Asking	MD concerns	Revisit list of concerns from beginning of the program.	10 min
Coaching	Conclusion	Conclude the program by assuring the physicians that they can document well. Ask them to apply the concepts they have learned between now and the next session and be prepared to share their experiences during the next session.	5 min

Figure 2.6. Contents of the Second Two-hour Educational Program for CAMP Method Training

Construct	Activity	Program Design to Foster Construct	Time
Coaching	Introduction	Review session outline and objectives. Physician instructor asks participants to share their documentation experiences over the past week. Provide feedback to examples.	15 min
Peer learning and coaching	DVD viewing	Have attendees view DVD of physicians discussing their concerns about documentation. At the completion of the video ask physicians to share their opinions of the documentation concepts shared in the DVD.	20 min
Mastering and coaching	Case study examples	Review cases studies 6–10 that correspond with objectives 1–6. Ask participants to comment on the examples. Provide feedback on comments.	15 min
Asking	Break	Serve refreshments and take a 5-minute break allowing participants to interact with each other.	10 min
Mastering and coaching	Case study exercises	Give physicians case study exercises 6–10 that contain documentation from actual patient records to review and provide the correct documentation to identify the patients' diagnoses. Review answers with physicians asking participants for their responses. Provide feedback as each participant shares answers.	15 min
Mastering, peer learning, coaching, and asking	Tools	Ask physicians to refer to their *Clinical Documentation Improvement Handbook* and *Doc Pocket Tool*. Ask participants to provide examples of where and when they were able to use either tool over the past week (since the first session). Provide feedback on the use of the tools as shared by the participants. Use any remaining time to review the contents of the handbook again.	15 min
Asking	Resident commitment	Review listing of concerns generated by residents during previous session. Identify how their dedication and commitment to medicine can be demonstrated through good documentation practices. Ask the residents to sign a "Commitment to Improved Clinical Documentation form."	10 min
	Post-test	Have participants take the self-assessment and the post-test. Collect the self-assessments and the post-tests. Review the answers with the participants.	15 min
Coaching	Conclusion	Conclude the program by assuring the physicians that they can document well.	5 min
Peer learning and coaching	Evaluation	Ask participants to evaluate the educational program.	2 min

Figure 2.7. Summary of Hypotheses Results

Hypothesis	Independent Variable	Dependent Variable	Statistical Significance*	Effect size/ Adj R² Difference**
H1: Clinical documentation self-efficacy has a direct, positive effect on clinical documentation quality	Clinical documentation self-efficacy	Participants' documentation quality score	>0.05	.004
H2: Coaching, asking, mastering, and peer learning have a direct, positive effect on clinical documentation quality	CAMP Method training	Participants' clinical documentation quality score	< 0.05	.527
H3: Coaching, asking, mastering, and peer learning have a direct, positive effect on clinical documentation self-efficacy	CAMP Method training	Participants' self-efficacy score	< 0.05	.083
H4: Coaching and asking have a direct, positive effect on clinical documentation quality	Limited training	Participants' clinical documentation quality score	< 0.05	.203
H5: Coaching and asking have a direct, positive effect on clinical documentation self-efficacy	Limited training	Participants' self-efficacy score	>0.05	.005
H6: The positive effect of exposure to coaching, asking, mastering, and peer learning on clinical documentation quality is greater than the positive effect of exposure to only coaching and asking	CAMP Method or limited training	Participants' clinical documentation quality score	< 0.05	.317
H7: Clinical documentation self-efficacy positively moderates the relationship between coaching, asking, mastering, and peer learning and clinical documentation quality	CAMP Method training	Participants' clinical documentation quality score	>0.05	.006
H8: Clinical documentation self-efficacy positively moderates the relationship between coaching and asking and clinical documentation quality	Limited training	Participants' clinical documentation quality score	> 0.05	.004

* Significance level: p < 0.05
** High effect size = .40; Medium effect size = .30; Low effect size = .10

(Highlighted rows indicate a hypothesis that was found to be statistically significant.)

there were no obvious reasons to believe these would be confounding factors in the study findings.

In summary, no genuine threats to the validity of the CAMP Method study are apparent.

CHAPTER SUMMARY

The CAMP Method study was conducted using rigorous research methods to test six hypotheses regarding the relationship between CAMP Method or limited training and clinical documentation quality and two hypotheses regarding the relationship between CAMP Method or limited training and clinical documentation self-efficacy. The use of coaching, asking, mastering, and peer learning (CAMP) was tested for its ability to improve clinical documentation quality and clinical documentation self-efficacy. Data from three pre- and postintervention questionnaires were programmed into linear regression models. The results of the statistical analysis showed that the CAMP Method training improves both clinical documentation quality and clinical documenta-tion self-efficacy. While the analysis showed that the 90-minute limited training group's documentation quality improved, it was significantly less than the improvement seen in the CAMP Method group's docu-mentation. Furthermore, the models showed no statistically significant relationship between the limited training and the physician's clinical documentation self-efficacy.

STEPS YOU CAN TAKE TODAY

- Share the study methodology with some physicians you know who have an interest in research. Ask them for their opinions.
- Review your own methods for training physicians in clinical documentation principles and determine how it compares to the training described in the CAMP Method.
- Discuss the section on overall and specific objectives for clinical documentation provided in the chapter with a colleague and com-pare it with your current program objectives, if you have one.

3. Peer Learning

PEER LEARNING involves instruction by a knowledgeable peer. In this case, the physician is learning by observing and listening to other physicians who are knowledgeable about high quality clinical documentation. Because it may be difficult to identify a physician who has both high quality clinical documentation skills and the ability to instruct on the topic, you can use a team approach like that used in the study. The study used a physician–Health Information Management (HIM) professional instructor team. The physician, a family practice medicine specialist, was knowledgeable in high quality clinical documentation and the clinical documentation expert was an MPH- and PhD-prepared HIM professional.

This chapter will describe who should provide the training and how the training should be delivered in order to ensure the *peer learning* component of the CAMP™ Method is achieved. The closer your organization's training is to the training design used in the study, the more likely you will be able to produce similar, sustainable results.

WHO TRAINS?

The primary focus in the selection of trainers is to fulfill the self-efficacy requirement for vicarious learning, or *peer learning*. Essentially, the criteria requires that trainees are instructed by knowledgeable peers. The peer requirement is key because, under the theory of self-efficacy, individuals are more likely to learn and retain information when it is delivered by someone who has a professional background and experiences similar to those of the trainees. So for physicians, being trained by a physician is essential to the success of the training.

The criteria still requires, however, that the training be provided by someone who is knowledgeable. For physicians in particular, instruction by someone without depth of knowledge on a subject, even if that individual is a physician, may result in a reversal of the learning process. Therefore, the instructor must either have significant depth of knowledge or be teamed with another credible individual who can complement the physician's knowledge level. But even if the physician is teamed with a clinical documentation expert, the physician must still have more than a basic operating knowledge of the clinical documentation process. At a minimum, the physician instructor must have the skills listed in figure 3.1.

Because there are few physicians today who meet the ideal skill sets to be an instructor of clinical documentation, it is likely that most organizations will need to team up a physician who has the minimum skill set with a nonphysician instructor. The skill set of the nonphysician instructor is also important. The recommendations for ideal and minimum skill sets for nonphysician instructors are listed in figure 3.2. A minimum skill set for the nonphysician instructor is provided since these individuals could serve as adjuncts to a physician and nonphysician instructor with ideal skill sets when the physicians in a training program number more than 30.

BRINGING IN OTHER PHYSICIANS

Because every organization will not have the internal resources to meet even the minimum recommendations for instructors, it is important to have other options available. One option for every organization would be to bring in outside experts to provide the training. Another option is to team up your organization's internal physicians with external instructors so you can eventually build a team of physicians who are capable of providing the regular support for clinical documentation training within your organization. In one organization, the physician leaders for clinical documentation were chosen because of their leadership abilities, not knowledge of documentation principles or ability to teach.

Figure 3.1. Skills Required of Physician Clinical Documentation Instructor

Skill	Physician instructor *ideal*	Physician instructor *minimum*
Professional training	Currently licensed MD or DO; board certified in specialty of physicians in the training group	Currently licensed MD or DO
Training in clinical documentation	At least 40 hours; certification if possible	At least 40 hours
Experience in clinical documentation	Five years of practice; currently treating patients	Three years of practice; currently treating patients on at least a part-time basis
Experience providing classroom instruction	At least 40 hours of instruction	At least 40 hours of instruction
Experience providing practical instruction	At least 100 hours of on-unit or in-office observation and feedback	At least 40 hours of on-unit or in-office observation and feedback

Figure 3.2. Skills Required of Nonphysician Clinical Documentation Instructor

Skill	Nonphysician instructor *ideal*	Nonphysician instructor *minimum*
Formal education	Bachelor's degree or above in a clinical area; current licensure or accreditation; academic training in pathophysiology and health information	Bachelor's degree or equivalent with licensure or accreditation in a clinical or healthcare area
Training in clinical documentation	At least 80 hours and certification, if possible	At least 80 hours
Experience in clinical documentation	Experience documenting in patient records; at least five years reviewing documentation in patient records	At least five years reviewing documentation in patient records
Experience providing classroom instruction	At least 40 hours of instruction	At least 40 hours of instruction
Experience providing practical instruction	At least 160 hours of on-unit or in-office observation and feedback	At least 100 hours of on-unit or in-office observation and feedback

The physician leaders attended all of the clinical documentation instruction provided to the technical specialists, which was over 100 hours. During the physician training sessions, the internal physician leaders were present to show support. In the beginning, they provided the introduction and spoke on the importance of clinical documentation. However, within the year, the internal physician leaders were able to act as adjuncts to the consulting experts during the follow-up training sessions. By the second year of the clinical documentation program, the internal physician leaders, with support from the consulting firm, were able to conduct almost all of the follow-up training sessions on their own. In the end, these physicians met the criteria for the *ideal* skill set for a physician clinical documentation instructor.

TOOLS

Clinical documentation tools were provided to participants during the study. As part of the training, participants received the following items:

- A copy of the PowerPoint slides used during instruction
- A copy of case studies 1 through 10
- One *Clinical Documentation Improvement Handbook*[1]
- One *Doc Pocket Tool* for their specialty[2]

It is essential that the instructor or instructional team can clearly explain these tools and respond to questions about the tools. The tools were given to the participants toward the end of the first session. The instructors reviewed the tools and explained how to use them. The participants were asked to use the tools in the 7 to 10 day period between the first and second training sessions, and to return with any questions they might have about them.

SUPPORT OUTSIDE THE CLASSROOM

It is essential that support be provided for trainees outside of the classroom setting. The best programs provide ongoing support in the form of trained clinical documentation professionals whose primary function is to review records for documentation defects and interact with the physician, when needed, to obtain high quality clinical documentation. However, it is also important to have physician peer instructors available for questions. These physicians could be available via phone or e-mail on an ongoing basis. However, during any focused training of more than 10 to 12 physicians, either internal or external physician peer instructors should be available on the nursing units of the hospital, or locally within a clinic setting, to answer questions. Teaching hospitals and academic medical centers will also have this need when new residents begin their work each summer.

TRAINING THE TRAINER

It is important for both operational and compliance purposes that every organization provides training for its internal physician trainers. Unless you plan to hire outside experts to come to your organization on a regular basis for ongoing training, you will need to structure a train-the-trainer arrangement. In the section on bringing in other physicians, above, an informal method for training the trainers is described. There, the internal physician leaders of the clinical documentation program attended all training sessions provided by the outside consulting firm. They also observed and participated in on-unit documentation training. By the end of a year, the internal leaders were able to take over the organization's training process.

PHYSICIAN ACTIVITIES DURING THE TRAINING PROCESS

During the training process, the physician instructor should use a few methods to demonstrate his knowledge of high quality clinical documentation practices. One approach would be to document a few diagnoses on the whiteboard. Another possibility would be for the physician to document diagnoses that do not meet high quality criteria, followed by documenting a sample that does meet high quality criteria. In addition, the physician will need to thoroughly explain the documentation. For example, the physician could initially document the diagnosis of *pneumonia*. Then he could explain that the patient's record shows symptoms of aspiration on diagnostic testing. So the physician can change the diagnosis to *aspiration pneumonia*. There are several examples in the PowerPoint slides that could be referenced. While the physician could always discuss the slides, the actual process of a physician documenting the diagnosis strengthens the self-efficacy component for the trainees.

The physician instructors should also tell stories about documentation problems they have personally encountered in the past, and how they overcame those problems. These may be simple examples involving legibility, or more detailed and specific examples like the aspiration pneumonia example above. The important point for cultivating self-efficacy is that the physician tells a story showing how *his* documentation improved as a result of applying the principles that the physician trainees are learning in the program.

Listed below are the objectives of the documentation training program for the first session:

1. Demonstrate an understanding of the relationship between physician documentation and the translation of that documentation into ICD-9-CM coded data.
2. Demonstrate an understanding that ICD-9-CM coded data is used for planning, reimbursement, quality ratings, Medicare Conditions of Participation, Joint Commission Core Measures, and research.
3. Provide documentation in the inpatient record that is timely, legible, complete, clear, consistent, reliable, and precise.
4. Document detail and precision in the patient's principal diagnosis.
5. Document all chronic coexisting secondary diagnoses.
6. Document all acute coexisting secondary diagnoses.
7. Document the clinical significance of all abnormal diagnostic tests.
8. Document the etiology or suspected etiology of symptoms.

Listed below are the objectives for the second documentation session:

1. Review basic documentation concepts from session one.
2. Discuss opportunities to improve documentation since session one.
3. Provide documentation in the inpatient record that is timely, legible, complete, clear, consistent, reliable, and precise.
4. Document detail and precision in the patient's principal diagnosis.
5. Document all chronic coexisting secondary diagnoses.
6. Document all acute coexisting secondary diagnoses.
7. Document the clinical significance of all abnormal diagnostic tests.
8. Document the etiology or suspected etiology of symptoms.

During the intervening 7 to 10 day period between the first session and the second training session, the physician instructor should ask the trainees to spend some time observing others documenting. Trainees should also reflect on their own documentation in light of the principles they learned during session one. The trainees should be prepared to share their experiences with the class during session two. They should also be prepared to give at least one example of how they modified their documentation practice during the past week because of something they learned during the first session.

SAMPLE CASE STUDIES FROM POWERPOINT PRESENTATIONS

The training program PowerPoint slides provide 10 case studies. While you can modify the specific content to reflect your own patient mix, it is important to make sure that you match up all of the case studies with the objectives of the program. Currently, the case study subject matter addresses all of the objectives, so any changes you make to the PowerPoint presentations from the first two sessions should be minimal. Two examples of case studies that are described by the physician instructors are provided below.

Case Study 1

Patient with a long history of metastatic colon cancer admitted now for weakness. For the past month, patient has been unable to eat and has lost 18 pounds. In addition, over the past few days patient has been nauseated and vomiting several times a day. Final diagnosis: weakness, weight loss, history of colon cancer.

If the physician documents *malnutrition* as the principal diagnosis (or cause of weakness) with *dehydration* as a secondary diagnosis (CC), *if clincally indicated and appropriate*, this documentation will impact:

- Coding
- Reimbursement
- Severity of illness
- Healthcare report card ratings

Case Study 2

Patient is admitted with syncope. Patient was worked up neurologically with no significant findings. Patient had a long standing history of hypertension and bradycardia. EKGs during stay noted bradycardia for which patient was promptly treated. Echo revealed moderate mitral regurgitation and trivial aortic stenosis. Diagnosis documented by the physician: syncope.

If the physician documents *bradycardia* as the cause of syncope and *mitral regurgitation* as a secondary diagnosis *if clincally indicated and appropriate*, this documentation will impact:

- Coding
- Reimbursement
- Severity of illness
- Healthcare report card ratings

COMPLIANCE AND THE 10 RULES OF CLINICAL DOCUMENTATION

The PowerPoint instructional material also includes *10 Rules of Clinical Documentation* that are addressed in both the first and the second session. The 10 rules, along with the seven quality criteria, provide significant, compliant structure for the physicians to follow in their own documenting. In addition, they also provide your organization with the basis for generating compliant queries to physicians about their documentation. For example, as long as queries are only asked when one of the seven criteria for high quality clinical documentation is not met, then the query itself should be compliant. Methodology for raising a query is addressed in the chapter on the physician–clinical documentation specialist relationship. But, minimally, if the physician is trained in high quality documentation methods, follows those methods, and is responsible for her own documentation, then what she documents should be compliant.

For many years physicians have been asked to clarify their documentation in patient records. Until recently, much of the questioning occurred in the health information management department after the patient was discharged. While this was a necessary activity, it was not, and is not, an optimal way to obtain high quality clinical documentation. Ideally, complete documentation should be provided while the patient is being treated. In the old-school method of asking physicians to answer questions after discharge, the physicians often felt they were in a passive role. This was not the intent in questioning. But because physicians were not trained to be high quality documenters, they did not feel like they *owned* the function of documenting, and, in particular, the function of correcting or modifying documentation after the fact. In these situations, physicians would sometimes ask the health information professional for her opinion. Although the HIM professional would not respond, the fact that the physician felt he needed her guidance to clarify his documentation was problematic.

The compliant way to ensure high quality clinical documentation is to train physicians on the process so they have high self-efficacy in their documentation practices. If so, they will be more likely to take an active role in documenting correctly the first time—and answering using their own internal logic trees, should they be asked to clarify their documentation because it does not meet one or more of the quality criteria. The best way for any organization to ensure physicians are proactive in their attitude towards documentation is to train physician trainers as well as the physicians themselves. Consequently, train-the-trainer programs are essential to maintaining high quality clinical documentation in any healthcare organization.

The 10 rules of clinical documentation included in the training materials are to document:

- Legibly
- Concurrently with the patient's visit/treatment
- Diagnostic etiology, not just symptoms; if necessary include ruled out diagnoses
- Every secondary chronic condition/diagnosis
- Every secondary acute condition/diagnosis
- Diagnosis/es or possible diagnoses for every medication ordered
- Diagnosis/es or possible diagnoses for every test ordered
- Diagnosis/es or possible diagnoses for every abnormal test result
- The response to every query in a complete and timely manner
- Detail, adjectives, and any other descriptors for a diagnosis

COURSE CONTENT

An overview of the course content for the first and second training sessions are provided in figures 3.3 and 3.4. In particular, each activity is linked up to a component of physician self-efficacy (peer learning, coaching, mastering, and/or asking) to demonstrate how the program content flows along with self-efficacy theory components to ensure physicians have the optimal training experience. In figures 3.3 and 3.4, the areas highlighted in gray use peer learning during the activity.

CHAPTER SUMMARY

The peer learning component of the CAMP Method involves physicians training physicians. Physician trainers must have certain characteristics and experiences to ensure optimal outcomes consistent with the training study findings. Optimal qualifications include being a licensed and board certified MD or DO who is currently practicing medicine, at least part-time. In addition, the physician trainer should have completed at

Figure 3.3. Course Contents of the First Two-hour Educational Program for CAMP Method Training Highlighting Peer Learning Use During the Activity

Concept	Activity	Program Design to Foster Construct	Time
Peer learning and coaching	Introduction	Review session outline and objectives. Physician instructor shares own experience with clinical documentation and assures participants that, with the appropriate training and support, they will master this process.	10 min
Mastering	Self-assessment and test	Participants take the self-assessment and the pre-test. Collect the self-assessment and the pre-test from the participants before reviewing the responses.	10 min
Peer learning	Test review	Review test questions and correct responses with attendees.	10 min
Asking	Resident commitment to good clinical documentation	Discuss the relationship between good documentation practices and improved patient outcomes with the participants. Ask physicians to share their concerns about clinical documentation. Make a list of what they are and share the list (as a way to end this portion of the session). State that we will revisit the list in the second session. Include time management if not addressed by physicians.	10 min
Peer learning	Documentation rules	Review documentation "rules" PowerPoint with physicians. Ask for and allow questions throughout this portion of the presentation.	15 min
Asking	Break	Serve refreshments and take a 5-minute break.	10 min
Peer learning and mastering	Case study examples	Review case studies 1–5 that correspond with objectives 2–5.	15 min
Mastering	Tools	Provide each physician with a *Clinical Documentation Improvement Handbook* and a *Doc Pocket Tool.* Review the contents of the *Handbook* and the *Tool.* Allow for questions throughout this portion of the presentation.	15 min
Mastering and asking	Case study exercises	Give physicians case study exercises 1–5 that contain documentation from actual patient records to review and provide the correct documentation to identify the patient's diagnosis/es. Review answers with physicians asking participants for their responses. Provide feedback as each participant shares his answers.	15 min
Asking	MD concerns	Revisit list of concerns from beginning of the program.	10 min
Coaching	Conclusion	Conclude the program by assuring the physicians that they can document well. Ask them to apply the concepts they have learned between now and the next session, and be prepared to share their experiences during the next session.	5 min

Figure 3.4. Contents of the Second Two-hour Educational Program for CAMP Method Training Highlighting Peer Learning Use During the Activity

Construct	Activity	Program Design to Foster Construct	Time
Coaching	Introduction	Review session outline and objectives. Return the pre-test results to each participant. Physician instructor asks participants to share their documentation experiences over the past week. Provide feedback to examples.	15 min
Peer learning and coaching	DVD viewing	Have attendees view DVD of physicians discussing their concerns about documentation. At the completion of the video ask physicians to share their opinions of the documentation concepts shared in the DVD.	20 min
Mastering and coaching	Case study examples	Review cases studies 6–10 that correspond with objectives 1–6. Ask participants to comment on the examples. Provide feedback on comments.	15 min
Asking	Break	Serve refreshments and take a 5-minute break allowing participants to interact with each other.	10 min
Mastering and coaching	Case study exercises	Give physicians case study exercises 6–10 that contain documentation from actual patient records to review and provide the correct documentation to identify the patients' diagnoses. Review answers with physicians asking participants for their responses. Provide feedback as each participant shares answers.	15 min
Mastering, peer learning, coaching, and asking	Tools	Ask physicians to refer to their *Clinical Documentation Improvement Handbook* and *Doc Pocket Tool*. Ask participants to provide examples of where and when they were able to use either tool over the past week (since the first session). Provide feedback on the use of the tools as shared by the participants. Use any remaining time to review the contents of the book again.	15 min
Asking	Resident commitment	Review listing of concerns generated by residents during previous session. Identify how their dedication and commitment to medicine can be demonstrated through good documentation practices. Ask the residents to sign a "Commitment to Improved Clinical Documentation form."	10 min
	Post-test	Have participants take the self-assessment and the post-test. Collect the self-assessments and the post-tests. Review the answers with the participants.	15 min
Coaching	Conclusion	Conclude the program by assuring the physicians that they can document well.	5 min
Asking	Evaluation	Ask participants to evaluate the educational program.	2 min

least 40 hours of training in clinical documentation, provided at least 40 hours of instruction, and at least 100 hours of on-unit observation and feedback of others. Because a physician will be highly unlikely to address all of the issues in the clinical documentation training sessions, it is best to pair up the physician with a clinical documentation expert. Ideal criteria for this individual are provided in the chapter.

Other important activities to reinforce the peer learning concept include training the trainer, bringing in outside physician experts, and using case studies and personal examples to demonstrate knowledge of the subject matter. The CAMP Method training is provided during two 2-hour sessions. Peer learning activities are programmed throughout the training session. In addition, the physician trainer should take advantage of any opportunities for additional coaching that come up during the training sessions.

STEPS YOU CAN TAKE TODAY

- Review the criteria for physician and nonphysician trainers and determine how close your current clinical documentation training team comes to meeting these criteria.
- If you do not yet have a clinical documentation program, determine who in your organization has the right background to be a trainer.
- Review both the objectives and the educational program course contents for session one and session two. Then determine how many of these objectives and educational activities are included in your current clinical documentation training program.

4. Mastering

MASTERING involves practical application of the principles discussed and demonstrated during the training program. Here, the physicians who are participating in training successfully practice and provide high quality clinical documentation as part of the training process. Training materials are presented ranging from the least complex to the more complex to ensure effective results. Although all four elements of the CAMP™ Method are required to obtain the best and most sustainable results, *mastering* is the most important single element of the four. As shown by the limited training group outcomes, without mastering, proficiency levels are likely to be 15 points (or 20 percent) lower. Of even greater interest is the fact that few organizations, if any, provide clinical documentation training to physicians with the mastering component included. The theory of self-efficacy incorporates a long-tested theory of adult learning that identifies mastery of an activity as the most important training component. In order to master an activity, the concepts must be applied. And peer learning, asking, and coaching are essential support activities.

There are many reasons why organizations do not provide mastering components in the training of physicians. These include time constraints and the unwillingness of the physicians to cooperate with requests for more detailed documentation. However, physicians themselves were trained in medical school using the mastering concept, as well as the peer learning concept. Without mastering during medical school, physicians would be expected to treat patients without ever training to know exactly how to perform a history and physical, what tests to prescribe, what medications to order, and so on. Ultimately, training in clinical documentation for physicians using thorough educational programs that include the mastering concept will occur only when organizations are committed to the importance of high quality clinical documentation. The reasons why executive teams at healthcare organizations should include high quality clinical documentation in their strategy are addressed in chapters 1 and 3 of volume 1.

In this chapter, we will describe the specific mastering activities that were tested during the study. These activities—and other similar, suggested activities—can be used to ensure that physicians achieve mastering skills during the training program.

MASTERING DEFINED

Mastery experience, also known as enactive attainment or performance accomplishment, is rooted in a person's own experience with success or failure. In mastery, participants successfully perform the particular task in question.[1] Self-efficacy—or being confident that you *can* do something *and then actually doing it*—can be achieved by including mastery practices within the training process. Desired competencies can be developed by breaking down complex skills into easily mastered subskills and organizing them hierarchically.

The CAMP Method begins the training process with the basic concepts of documentation and data. These concepts are first applied to simple case studies. Then, the same concepts are applied to more complex case studies, using actual sample medical record documentation. In this phase of the training, physicians are asked to review the documentation in the record, identify any documentation that does not meet quality criteria, and then document it themselves, consistent with acceptable criteria. Finally, during the intervening time between sessions one and two, physicians are asked to identify some opportunities they had to improve their own documentation. When the physicians return to session two, they are asked to share with the group specific details of how they improved their own documentation in a clinical setting. By establishing a connection between the training and the improved practice of clinical documentation, the mastery component of the training process is both highlighted and reinforced.

MASTERING PRACTICES USED IN THE CAMP METHOD CLINICAL DOCUMENTATION STUDY

The instructional methods for the mastering process were designed to optimally enhance self-efficacy. To meet this end, the precise content and timing of delivery are essential aspects of mastery training. The instructional sequence of the CAMP Method was very carefully arrived at to produce the most effective results in the mastery component. Because of this, the training sequence should be followed in order, and these activities are conducted during the first session:

1. Review of criteria for high quality clinical documentation.

This is a pure lecture activity that can be performed by the clinical documentation expert and the physician instructor together. PowerPoint slides are provided for each basic concept. In addition to the criteria for high quality documentation, the instructors review the use of documentation for coding purposes. There will be a general discussion about the use of clinical documentation for research, reimbursement, licensure, and planning. Figures 4.1 and 4.2 are examples of the slides used in the training that link clinical documentation to coding.

2. Review of documentation tools.

The *Clinical Documentation Physician Handbook* is provided to each participating physician. The table of contents is summarized with the group to reinforce the basic principles just reviewed by PowerPoint. Questions are raised and then answered.

3. Review of case summaries 1–5; asking for physician input.

Individual case summaries are included on PowerPoint slides. Each example shows a patient scenario that contains a documentation issue. The documentation issues demonstrate the principles just presented by the instructors. Preferably, the physician instructor will review the case summaries, reinforcing the peer learning component of the training as well as building on mastery. Physicians are asked to comment on the case summaries.

4. Physicians review and correct case studies 1 to 5 from sample medical records.

Five sample cases containing actual medical record documentation are provided to the physicians for their review. The cases were selected to emphasize the documentation principles taught thus far. The physicians are asked to identify any documentation *deficiencies* in the records—or any documentation that does not meet the seven criteria for high quality clinical documentation. After they have identified a deficiency, the physicians are asked to document the entry in the way it should be written. The cases are reviewed with the group and a different physician is asked to describe how she handled the case study.

5. Ask physicians to observe the documentation of other physicians when possible; and have them apply the criteria for high quality clinical documentation in practice, to their own documentation, before the next session.

The physicians can then share their experiences with the group during the second session.

The following activities should be conducted during the second session:

1. Discussion of the physicians' observations.

Here physicians are asked to describe the good documentation practices that they observed. And what did they observe that they would have done differently? This activity is used to fulfill both mastery and peer learning objectives for building self-efficacy.

2. Ask the physicians to describe any changes in their documentation practices.

Physicians are asked to share an example of how they changed their own documentation since the prior session, as a result of what they learned about high quality clinical documentation. If possible, each physician should share one item with the group.

Figure 4.1. Link Between Clinical Documentation and Coding

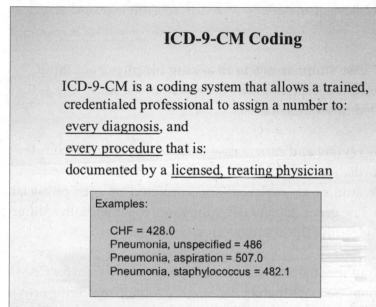

Figure 4.2. Link Between Clinical Documentation and Coding 2

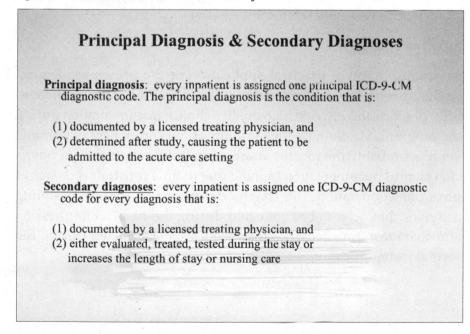

3. Re-review of criteria for high quality clinical documentation.

This is a review of material covered in session one and serves as reinforcement.

4. Review of case summaries 6 to 10 asking for physician input.

These case summaries should be presented in the same way as they were presented in session one.

5. Physicians review and *correct* case studies 6 to 10 from sample medical records.

These case studies are reviewed and corrected by each physician individually. The group then reviews the cases together with a different physician leading the discussion for each case.

Figure 4.3 outlines the first two-hour educational program for CAMP Method training. Sections highlighted in gray contain mastering activities and exercises for this session.

Figure 4.4 outlines the second two-hour educational program for CAMP Method training. Sections highlighted in gray contain mastering activities and exercises for this session.

CHAPTER SUMMARY

Mastering involves practical application of the principles demonstrated during the training sessions. The physician trainees successfully practice and provide high quality clinical documentation during the program. Mastering is the most important component of training; yet it is probably the practice most commonly excluded from physician clinical documentation training due to time constraints or lack of physician cooperation. This chapter describes five specific mastering activities that need to be conducted during the first training session and five mastering activities that need to be conducted during the second training session.

Figure 4.3. Course Contents of the First Two-hour Educational Program for CAMP Method Training Highlighting Mastering Activities and Exercises

Construct	Activity	Program Design to Foster Construct	Time
Peer learning and coaching	Introduction	Review session outline and objectives. Physician instructor shares own experience with clinical documentation and assures participants that, with the appropriate training and support, they will master this process.	10 min
Mastering	Self-assessment and test	Participants take the self-assessment and the pre-test. Collect the self-assessment and the pre-test from the participants before reviewing the responses.	10 min
Peer learning	Test review	Review test questions and correct responses with attendees.	10 min
Asking	Resident commitment to good clinical documentation	Discuss the relationship between good documentation practices and improved patient outcomes with the participants. Ask physicians to share their concerns about clinical documentation. Make a list of what they are and share the list (as a way to end this portion of the session). State that we will revisit the list in the second session. Include time management if not addressed by physicians.	10 min
Peer learning	Documentation rules	Review documentation "rules" PowerPoint with physicians. Ask for and allow questions throughout this portion of the presentation.	15 min
Asking	Break	Serve refreshments and take a 5-minute break.	10 min
Peer learning and mastering	Case study examples	Review cases studies 1–5 that correspond with objectives 2–5.	15 min
Mastering	Tools	Provide each physician with a *Clinical Documentation Improvement Handbook* and a *Doc Pocket Tool*. Review the contents of the handbook and the tool. Allow for questions throughout this portion of the presentation.	15 min
Mastering and asking	Case study exercises	Give physicians case study exercises 1–5 that contain documentation from actual patient records to review and provide the correct documentation to identify the patient's diagnosis/es. Review answers with physicians asking participants for their responses. Provide feedback as each participant shares his answers.	15 min
Asking	MD concerns	Revisit list of concerns from beginning of the program.	10 min
Coaching	Conclusion	Conclude the program by assuring the physicians that they can document well. Ask them to apply the concepts they have learned between now and the next session, and be prepared to share their experiences during the next session.	5 min

Figure 4.4. Contents of the Second Two-hour Educational Program for CAMP Method Training Highlighting Mastering Activities and Exercises

Construct	Activity	Program Design to Foster Construct	Time
Coaching	Introduction	Review session outline and objectives. Return the pre-test results to each participant. Physician instructor asks participants to share their documentation experiences over the past week. Provide feedback to examples.	15 min
Peer learning and coaching	DVD viewing	Have attendees view DVD of physicians discussing their concerns about documentation. At the completion of the video ask physicians to share their opinions of the documentation concepts shared in the DVD.	20 min
Mastering and coaching	Case study examples	Review cases studies 6–10 that correspond with objectives 1–6. Ask participants to comment on the examples. Provide feedback on comments.	15 min
Asking	Break	Serve refreshments and take a 5-minute break allowing participants to interact with each other.	10 min
Mastering and coaching	Case study exercises	Give physicians case study exercises 6–10 that contain documentation from actual patient records to review and provide the correct documentation to identify the patients' diagnoses. Review answers with physicians asking participants for their responses. Provide feedback as each participant shares answers.	15 min
Mastering, peer learning, coaching, and asking	Tools	Ask physicians to refer to their *Clinical Documentation Improvement Handbook* and *Doc Pocket Tool*. Ask participants to provide examples of where and when they were able to use either tool over the past week (since the first session). Provide feedback on the use of the tools as shared by the participants. Use any remaining time to review the contents of the book again.	15 min
Asking	Resident commitment	Review listing of concerns generated by residents during previous session. Identify how their dedication and commitment to medicine can be demonstrated through good documentation practices. Ask the residents to sign a "Commitment to Improved Clinical Documentation form."	10 min
	Post-test	Have participants take the self-assessment and the post-test. Collect the self-assessments and the post-tests. Review the answers with the participants.	15 min
Coaching	Conclusion	Conclude the program by assuring the physicians that they can document well.	5 min
Asking	Evaluation	Ask participants to evaluate the educational program.	2 min

STEPS YOU CAN TAKE TODAY

- Determine whether your current clinical documentation training program contains a mastering component. If not, what can you do to make sure that mastery is included?
- Review and discuss the five mastering activities for each clinical documentation training session with your colleagues. How does it compare to your current training program?

5. Coaching

COACHING involves grooming and encouraging participants about their abilities to perform high quality clinical documentation. The study identified what kinds of individuals can provide coaching to physicians and be well received. As might be imagined, the credibility, expertise, and trustworthiness of the person doing the persuading is of critical importance in the coaching process.[1] The study also identified when and how the coaching to physician trainees should be conducted in order to obtain optimal results. This methodology is designed not only to ensure that the physician improves her documentation, but that she feels in control of the process.

In this chapter, we will address the important qualifications that are needed by the trainer for effective coaching. In addition, we will describe how coaching was used during the training session, and how responses to the questionnaires were used to shape the coaching activities.

WHAT IS COACHING?

The third component of the CAMP™ Method is aimed at building a robust sense of self-efficacy to support the exercise of control in the face of difficulties that inevitably arise. Coaching helps the trainee strengthen his belief that he has the *ability* to provide high quality clinical documentation. This is achieved by incorporating repeated opportunities for guidance, encouragement, and corrective feedback into the process. Discussion about documentation experiences that occurred between the first and second sessions is important. In addition to scheduled coaching segments outlined in the training curriculum, coaching should be provided whenever the opportunity arises.

WHO IS THE COACH?

The coach must be an instructor who the physicians feel is credible and knowledgeable about the subject being taught. The best candidate for coaching is another physician with several years of clinical documentation practice and who is currently practicing medicine. The fact that the physician *currently* performs clinical documentation is important to most physician trainees. If the physician is instructing specialists, board certification in the same specialty will increase the trainee's confidence in the instructor, and his coaching abilities are more likely to have a positive impact. As noted in the section on mastering and peer learning, a second instructor who is a clinical documentation expert can co-train, particularly if the physician instructor has limited experience teaching clinical documentation. However, the nonphysician instructor alone cannot adequately perform the role of coach for a physician.

SPECIFIC OPPORTUNITIES FOR COACHING

There are specific times during the training program that work well for coaching activities. While the instructor can provide coaching whenever the opportunity arises, at a minimum, the following times should be used for coaching:

1. *In the introduction to the first session*: The physician instructor can use this opportunity to provide some initial positive feedback to the group about how they did on the tests and/or questionnaires and make a statement about their abilities to internalize this information and do well. Coaching should be low key at this point because of the limited experiences the participants have had with this instructor. The only exception to this would be if the instructor for the clinical documentation training has also trained the same group of physicians in other competencies. This may occur, for example, within residency programs.

2. *During the first session*: Right after the physician instructor asks the trainees for feedback about their concerns regarding clinical documentation and has vetted the comments, the trainer can interject some encouraging statements.

3. *At the conclusion of the first session*: People remember well what occurs last in an encounter. So every session should end on an upbeat, positive note. One of the best ways to do this is to acknowledge some achievement, comment, or correct answer from the participants and then reassure the group that they will be masters of clinical documentation by the end of the next session.

4. *At the beginning of the second session*: When trainees return for the second session and share their experiences in observing others and their own documentation practices during the past week, there will be many opportunities to interject positive feedback, reassurance, and encouraging statements.

5. *During the second session*: Towards the end of the first session, as part of the *asking* component, the instructors ask the participants to share their concerns about the clinical documentation practice. Towards the end of the second session, that list of concerns is brought out again by the instructors for re-review. Based on the participants' sharing of their experiences with documentation during the past week, how they responded to questions, case summaries, and case studies during the second class, and other comments, the instructor should be able to identify several opportunities for positive reinforcement.

6. *At the conclusion of the second session*: People remember well what occurs last in an encounter. End the training on an upbeat, positive note. One of the best ways to do this is to acknowledge some achievement, comment, or correct answer from the group and then reassure the group that they are and will continue to be masters of clinical documentation as long as they apply the concepts learned in this training and continue to be open to additional feedback and training opportunities.

USING SELF-EFFICACY QUESTIONNAIRE RESULTS TO GUIDE YOUR COACHING

In the study, the overall pre-training self-efficacy mean for the CAMP Method training group was 2.67 on a scale from 0 to 4. The post-training self-efficacy score for the same group was 2.89, an increase of .217. In contrast, the limited training group's self-efficacy increased by only .075 after training. And the control group's self-efficacy dropped by .089 after training. This finding further supports the conclusion that the specifics of the training process increase the trainee's self-efficacy. And since self-efficacy has a positive impact on learning and sustainability, using the CAMP Method for clinical documentation training is likely to produce a superior outcome for your organization.

You will not need to analyze the results of your self-efficacy questionnaire in this manner. However, you can use the responses to the questionnaire to prepare for the training program and guide your coaching activities. The instructors for the clinical documentation study used the responses to the questionnaire to focus on the content of the coaching process during training. Questions one and six asked the participants to rate their own clinical documentation on a scale from poor to excellent. This question appears in figure 5.1 and correlates to a score from 0 to 4. (See figure 5.1.) Prior to training, the initial self-quality rating mean was 2.30 (on a scale of 0 to 4). This score indicates that most of the participants rated themselves around a 2 or "good." No participants rated themselves *excellent* and few rated themselves *fair*. Going into the training session, it was helpful for the instructors to know how the group members viewed their own documentation. In the study, the fact that most participants viewed their documentation as *good* indicated that they were confident. However, when this information was combined with other responses—such as the little amount of training they previously had in clinical documentation, and their low level of confidence in documenting certain types of diagnoses or test results—it appeared that the self-quality ratings may have been artificially inflated.

In the next set of questions, listed in figure 5.2, participants were

Figure 5.1. Question 1 on Documentation

	Poor 0	Fair 1	Good 2	Very Good 3	Excellent 4
a. How would you rate the quality of your clinical documentation?					

asked to rate their level of confidence when it came to document-ing certain diagnoses and/or conditions in the patient's record. The physicians' highest level of confidence was in documenting acute conditions (mean = 3.47), while their lowest level of confidence was in documenting to meet Joint Commission regulations (mean = 2.07). A mean of less than 2.5 indicated to instructors the areas which could benefit from further coaching. In addition to the Joint Commission question, the mean was less than 2.5 for the following four questions: (1) the ability to document the patient's discharge summary within three days of discharge (mean = 2.23); (2) the ability to document the etiology or possible etiology of vertigo (mean = 2.40); (3) the ability to document in a way that would allow the hospital coder to accurately code the patient's diagnoses (mean = 2.30); and (4) the ability to meet Medicare documentation requirements (mean = 2.17). Going into the training program, the instructors were thus prepared to enhance the sections of the training on Medicare, the Joint Commission, and coding with some encouragement and coaching.

One way to begin this process is by having the instructors note that these are some of the same areas where *other* physicians feel they might need some additional training. The physician instructor can start off, for example, by using his own experiences as an example. The instructor may want to share that he also had a similar experience, but found, after some basic instruction, that he was able to internalize the information. And the coach can state that he believes the physicians in the training group will find similar results.

Some of the coaching activities intersect with the asking activities addressed in the next chapter. An example of coaching, asking, and peer learning is when a physician instructor relates his own experi-ences with documentation requirements for regulatory purposes, and

Figure 5.2. Questions 2–6 on Documentation

2. For my patients, I am confident that I can document in a hospital record:	Not at all	A little	Somewhat	Mostly	Completely
a. legibly					
b. a complete patient history and physical					
c. a history and physical within 24 hours of admission					
d. all of the patient's chronic conditions					
e. all of the patient's acute conditions					
f. the clinical significance of an abnormal diagnostic test					
g. the patient's diagnosis as interpreted on radiology reports					
h. the patient's diagnosis as interpreted on a path report					
i. the patient's diagnosis in the progress notes before discharge					
j. the patient's discharge summary within three days of discharge					
3. I am confident that I can document the etiology or possible etiology of a symptom for a patient who presents with:	Not at all	A little	Somewhat	Mostly	Completely
a. chest pain					
b. abdominal pain					
c. shortness of breath					
d. syncope					
e. vertigo					
4. I am confident that I can document the clinical significance of an abnormal:	Not at all	A little	Somewhat	Mostly	Completely
a. lab test					
b. EKG					
c. X-ray					
d. CT scan					
e. culture & sensitivity					
f. echocardiogram					

5. I am confident that I can document patient diagnoses in a way that will:	Not at all	A little	Somewhat	Mostly	Completely
a. allow the hospital coder to accurately code the patient's diagnoses					
b. meet Medicare documentation requirements					
c. meet Joint Commission documentation requirements					
	Poor	Fair	Good	Very Good	Excellent
6. Overall, how would you rate the quality of your clinical documentation?					

then assures the participants they will do fine, too, just as he did. The participants may begin to offer comments about the topic. At this point, the physician instructor can ask additional questions to identify any source of conflict or lack of support. By talking through the issue with the physicians to their own satisfaction, and reassuring them of their abilities, the instructor has bolstered the trainees' self-efficacy.

If your team is unable to analyze data prior to a training program, the CAMP Method study results can be used as a guideline. However, since results may vary, it is best to use data from the physicians to be trained in your own organization when developing a coaching strategy.

COURSE CONTENTS OF THE FIRST TWO-HOUR EDUCATIONAL PROGRAM FOR CAMP METHOD TRAINING

Coaching activities are highlighted in gray in the program outline shown in figure 5.3. There may be some overlapping activities with the asking component, depending on the feedback from participants. Remember, coaching deals with the trainee's beliefs in his *ability* to practice high quality clinical documentation. Asking addresses his *willingness* to provide it. Whenever the physician instructor finds an opportunity to reinforce, encourage, and coach, based on feedback from participants, he should take advantage of the opportunity.

Figure 5.3. Course Contents of the First Two-hour Educational Program for CAMP Method Training Highlighting Coaching Activities

Construct	Activity	Program Design to Foster Construct	Time
Peer learning and coaching	Introduction	Review session outline and objectives. Physician instructor shares own experience with clinical documentation and assures participants that, with the appropriate training and support, they will master this process.	10 min
Mastering	Self-assessment and test	Participants take the self-assessment and the pre-test. Collect the self-assessment and the pre-test from the participants before reviewing the responses.	10 min
Peer learning	Test review	Review test questions and correct responses with attendees.	10 min
Asking	Resident commitment to good clinical documentation	Discuss the relationship between good documentation practices and improved patient outcomes with the participants. Ask physicians to share their concerns about clinical documentation. Make a list of what they are and share the list (as a way to end this portion of the session). State that we will revisit the list in the second session. Include time management if not addressed by physicians.	10 min
Peer learning	Documentation rules	Review documentation "rules" PowerPoint with physicians. Ask for and allow questions throughout this portion of the presentation.	15 min
Asking	Break	Serve refreshments and take a 5-minute break.	10 min
Peer learning and mastering	Case study examples	Review cases studies 1–5 that correspond with objectives 2–5.	15 min
Mastering	Tools	Provide each physician with a *Clinical Documentation Improvement Handbook* and a *Doc Pocket Tool*. Review the contents of the *Handbook* and the *Tool*. Allow for questions throughout this portion of the presentation.	15 min
Mastering and asking	Case study exercises	Give physicians case study exercises 1–5 that contain documentation from actual patient records to review and provide the correct documentation to identify the patient's diagnosis/es. Review answers with physicians asking participants for their responses. Provide feedback as each participant shares his answers.	15 min
Asking	MD concerns	Revisit list of concerns from beginning of the program.	10 min
Coaching	Conclusion	Conclude the program by assuring the physicians that they can document well. Ask them to apply the concepts they have learned between now and the next session, and be prepared to share their experiences during the next session.	5 min

Figure 5.4. Course Contents of the Second Two-hour Educational Program for CAMP Method Training Highlighting Coaching Activities

Construct	Activity	Program Design to Foster Construct	Time
Coaching	Introduction	Review session outline and objectives. Return the pre-test results to each participant. Physician instructor asks participants to share their documentation experiences over the past week. Provide feedback to examples.	15 min
Peer learning and coaching	DVD viewing	Have attendees view DVD of physicians discussing their concerns about documentation. At the completion of the video ask physicians to share their opinions of the documentation concepts shared in the DVD.	20 min
Mastering and coaching	Case study examples	Review cases studies 6–10 that correspond with objectives 1–6. Ask participants to comment on the examples. Provide feedback on comments.	15 min
Asking	Break	Serve refreshments and take a 5-minute break allowing participants to interact with each other.	10 min
Mastering and coaching	Case study exercises	Give physicians case study exercises 6–10 that contain documentation from actual patient records to review and provide the correct documentation to identify the patients' diagnoses. Review answers with physicians asking participants for their responses. Provide feedback as each participant shares answers.	15 min
Mastering, peer learning, coaching, and asking	Tools	Ask physicians to refer to their *Clinical Documentation Improvement Handbook* and *Doc Pocket Tool*. Ask participants to provide examples of where and when they were able to use either tool over the past week (since the first session). Provide feedback on the use of the tools as shared by the participants. Use any remaining time to review the contents of the book again.	15 min
Asking	Resident commitment	Review listing of concerns generated by residents during previous session. Identify how their dedication and commitment to medicine can be demonstrated through good documentation practices. Ask the residents to sign a "Commitment to Improved Clinical Documentation form."	10 min
	Post-test	Have participants take the self-assessment and the post-test. Collect the self-assessments and the post-tests. Review the answers with the participants.	15 min
Coaching	Conclusion	Conclude the program by assuring the physicians that they can document well.	5 min
Asking	Evaluation	Ask participants to evaluate the educational program.	2 min

CONTENTS OF THE SECOND TWO-HOUR EDUCATIONAL PROGRAM FOR CAMP METHOD TRAINING

The coaching activities are highlighted in gray in figure 5.4. By the second session, there are some coaching opportunities in most program segments. This is based upon feedback from the participants and the anticipated flow of information back and forth between the instructor and the trainees during the second session.

CHAPTER SUMMARY

Coaching involves encouraging and grooming participants about their abilities to perform high quality clinical documentation. An effective coach should be viewed by the trainees as someone who is credible, trustworthy, and an expert on the topic. Because of this, physicians are generally the best coaches for other physicians. While there are six specific opportunities for coaching identified in the course outline, the physician instructor should provide additional coaching, as necessary, during the training sessions. Finally, to tailor the specific focus of the training, each organization should use the results of its self-efficacy questionnaire to customize the coaching component of its training program.

STEPS YOU CAN TAKE TODAY

- Identify two physicians on your medical staff who would be good physician coaches. They may be good candidates to become physician clinical documentation instructors.
- Discuss with colleagues what you believe would be the questions with the lowest scores on the clinical documentation self-efficacy questionnaire. If supported with test results, these areas are primary opportunities and focal points for physician coaching within your organization.

6. Asking

ASKING involves requesting feedback from the physician participants in a specific manner and at a specific time. It is essential that physicians have an opportunity to voice their concerns about what they are being asked to do. While coaching addresses the physician's *ability* to improve his clinical documentation (by offering encouragement), asking addresses his *willingness* to do it. Asking is designed to improve the physicians' documentation by helping them feel comfortable with the process. The physicians need to feel that their clinical documentation is not a forced process, but rather something they control. The ability of the physicians to provide open feedback about their concerns with the clinical documentation process will help to develop higher self-efficacy by confirming their desire to produce high quality documentation. The better the physicians' self-efficacy, the more in control they will feel, and the more likely they are to sustain their high quality clinical documentation practices—an important goal for every healthcare organization.

WHO ASKS?

Similar to coaching, it is important that the trainees feel the person who is providing feedback about the trainees' clinical documentation questions is a credible and knowledgeable individual. The best results occur with a physician instructor in the asking role. The trainee is more likely to find another physician's response more palatable than the response of a nonphysician, simply because the physician has had some of the same experiences as the trainee.

For example, during the clinical documentation study, one of the physician's concerns about the clinical documentation training was that he felt that the healthcare report cards did not apply to the physician. He could understand, he said, that they would apply to the hospital, but said that he felt he was being "fed a line" by the hospital about something that was irrelevant to him. The physician instructor addressed the question by describing his own quality ratings on HealthGrades. com. He talked about how his ratings were directly related to the two hospitals where he had admission privileges. And furthermore, since one of the hospitals had low ratings for pneumonia, he was concerned that the rating might have a negative impact on him. The instructor was then able to relate his documentation in that hospital to the clinical documentation and coding that became the basis for those ratings. Although the physician instructor did not have concrete proof at the time he was speaking, the instructor felt certain that the changes he and his colleagues made to be more precise and complete in their documentation would translate to better outcomes for the hospital in the next year. It appeared as though the physician trainee was satisfied with this response. And, in fact, several trainees nodded their heads as the physician instructor described his own experiences. This example of the asking component of the CAMP™ Method also illustrates the peer learning component. One recommended approach to the training process is to use as many of the CAMP Method components as possible when the opportunity arises. The more CAMP Method concepts that are employed during the training process, the more likely there will be a superior result.

WHAT IS ASKING?

Asking is much more than just posing the question, "What are your concerns about clinical documentation?" That is a starting point, but the instructor's didactic skills become apparent during the ensuing interaction. The participant states his concern. The instructor may need to clarify or ask follow-up questions, but he needs to eventually comment on the concern. The comment may be as simple as, "I understand your concern and it is valid." In most situations, however, the physician instructor will need to provide a more substantive reply. He may need to give examples, use his own experience, identify possible solutions, or ask the physician attendees to identify their own solutions. If so, the physician instructor will then need to comment on the trainee's proposed solution. The key skill set for the asking section is the ability to manage the trainees so that the instructor allows them to vet, provides direction or a solution, and then moves onto the next concern. Instructors should identify possible concerns of the group either through presession conversations or by reviewing the attitudes and opinions questionnaires before the session. This will allow instructors to prepare possible responses and, if the issues are large enough, have conversations with the administration beforehand.

SPECIFIC OPPORTUNITIES TO USE THE ASKING COMPONENT

The ultimate purpose of the asking component is to ease the physician trainees' concerns and clear their minds so they can learn with confidence. Use the following suggestions to make the asking component, and the overall training program, more effective:

1. *Location.* The setting is important to allaying concerns. The basics like location, noise level, and the ability to focus and not be disturbed, have an important impact on the ability to learn. This is not a novel concept; however, in the hospital setting, quiet, focused sessions in nice surroundings are not the norm. Being able to secure a quality location and asking physicians to turn off pagers and phones sets the tone for the importance of the meeting. In a healthcare system in New York City, the research team provided training to a group of cardiothoracic surgeons for five hours straight. The chief of the service who requested the training was dedicated to showing his support for the topic, so he arranged to have us meet in the hospital board room, and he had lunch brought in and served. I was certain that pagers and phones would be going off and the physicians would not be focused on the topic. In fact, all electronic devices were turned off and the session went on continuously without anyone leaving, even to

use the restroom. By providing such a high quality experience, the importance of the training became obvious. If an entire team of cardiothoracic surgeons can dedicate five hours each to the activity, any physician group can do the same.

2. *Organization.* Similarly, the organization of the session plays an important role in showing physicians that you are serious about the importance of this topic. The more smoothly the session flows, the less likely physicians are to express concerns.

3. *Give them food and drink.* As Abraham Maslow noted in his hierarchy of needs, without the basics, you cannot expect human beings to achieve the next level of functioning. You don't want your participants to be hungry and thirsty while they are trying to learn. If you provide food and drink, you are eliminating concerns about basic needs.

4. *Ask about concerns during the first session.* The instructor should ask the physician trainees to address their concerns about clinical documentation during the end of the first training session. At this point, the participants will have had enough instruction to begin identifying concerns they may have in addition to any problems they may have brought with them. The instructor should manage some discussion around each point of concern.

5. *Write concerns on a board.* The instructor should write each concern on a board so the participants can see as well as hear them. This will ensure that you cover all of their concerns and sends a strong message that you take them seriously.

6. *Revisit concerns during the second session.* Use the board from the first session to remind the trainees about the concerns they had voiced previously. At this point, ask if they have any more concerns to add, or if they have different feelings about the issues they originally mentioned. The participants had expressed concerns about finding adequate time to document during the first session. However, in the second session, after applying the concepts in their own documentation practices, many of the physician trainees said they were no longer worried about time being an issue.

7. *Bring in support.* Depending on the extent of the concerns, during

Figure 6.1. Summary of Physicians' Concerns

Summary of physicians' concerns about providing high quality clinical documentation
1. Not enough education on topic during medical school or residency program
2. Time constraints, not enough time to document more
3. No financial incentive because salaries are fixed
4. Healthcare report card ratings are irrelevant to us
5. Templates can result in too much cutting and pasting and irrelevant information
6. Documentation doesn't really impact patient care, does it?

the second session you may want to bring in members of the administration or senior physicians in the organization to address issues that were raised. In one case, we had a group of physicians who had significant concerns about the hospital's access for electronic medical record entries. If we had not addressed the issue further, the concern might have been large enough to have a negative impact on the trainees' self-efficacy, thereby negating any positive impact from the training. In this case, the chief information officer and the chief operating officer of the hospital attended the second session and shared some plans with physicians for purchasing new terminals and a timeline for roll out. It was important that the hospital executives were not just there to pay lip service to the training session; they had to show the physician trainees credible evidence of the solutions they were putting into place.

PHYSICIANS' CONCERNS IDENTIFIED DURING THE CLINICAL DOCUMENTATION STUDY

The educational program provided social and psychological support for the desired change in clinical documentation practice skills by providing a meal just before the session, discussing and giving examples of the patient quality and care issues that can be impacted by their documentation, and allowing attendees to express their concerns and fears about their ability to provide high quality clinical documentation. Figure 6.1 lists concerns identified by the physician attendees during this discussion. Because time management is an issue for all physicians, time management and efficiencies in documentation were discussed in detail during the session.

TRAINEES' RESPONSES TO THE OPEN-ENDED QUESTIONNAIRE

Part of the self-efficacy questionnaire used in the clinical documentation study was a section that contained open-ended questions about strengths, weaknesses, facilitators of, and barriers to good clinical documentation. The physician trainees' answers to these questions are helpful to the instructors in preparing responses to the coaching and asking components of the program. They can also help every healthcare organization understand what it may be able to do to improve physician documentation apart from, or in addition to, training.

An analysis of the responses to open-ended questions was performed by the researchers for the clinical documentation study. The results of these analyses are provided in figure 6.2. For question 7 (What do you consider to be your strengths when it comes to clinical documentation?), three key phrases were identified. These phrases were (1) *legible handwriting*, (2) *all/differential diagnoses*, and (3) *thoroughness*. These phrases appear in 21, 35, and 37 percent of the questions, respectively. Almost a third of the residents believe their handwriting is legible, that they are documenting all of the possible differential diagnoses, and that they are thorough in their documentation. For question number 8 (What do you consider to be your weaknesses when it comes to clinical documentation?), two key phrases or words were identified. These phrases were (1) *listing all diagnoses* and (2) *legibility*. Forty-one percent of the residents believed that they were weak when it came to listing all diagnoses for a patient. And 28 percent believed clinical documentation in general is not legible. Comparing responses to question 7 with responses to question 8, it appears that while residents believe their own documentation is legible, they also believe that other documentation in the patient record is *not* legible. In addition, about half of the residents believe they are thorough in documenting all diagnoses while half believe they are weak at listing all diagnoses.

For question number 9 (What do you believe facilitates good clinical documentation?), two key phrases or words were identified. These

Figure 6.2. Open-Ended Clinical Documentation Questions

1. What do you consider to be your strengths when it comes to clinical documentation?

2. What do you consider to be your weaknesses when it comes to clinical documentation?

3. What do you believe facilitates good clinical documentation?

4. What do you believe are barriers to good clinical documentation?

5. What are your suggestions for improving physicians' clinical documentation?

Figure 6.3. Analysis of Responses to Open-Ended Questions

Question #	Word/Phrase	# times appeared	% of time
7	Legible handwriting	19	20.8%
7	All/differential diagnoses	32	35.2%
7	Thoroughness	34	37.4%
8	Listing all diagnoses	37	40.7%
8	Legibility	25	27.5%
9	Time to document	59	64.8%
10	Lack of time	18	19.8%
11	Education/training	31	34.1%
11	Feedback	14	15.4%
11	Electronic/computerized medical records	12	13.2%

phrases were (1) *legibility* and (2) *time to document*. When compared with the one key phrase identified in question 10 (What do you believe are barriers to good clinical documentation?), which was *lack of time*, it is clear that the residents believe that they need more time to provide high quality clinical documentation. They also believe that they currently do not have sufficient time to document well.

For question 11 (What are your suggestions for improving physicians' clinical documentation?), three key phrases or terms were identified. They are: (1) *education/training*, (2) *feedback*, and (3) *electronic/computerized medical records*. The most commonly used phrase in response to this question was the "need for education," which was used by 34 percent of the residents. The most commonly used phrase overall was "time to document," which was used by 64.8 percent of the residents. The term used in the greatest number of responses was "legibility," which was found to be a common key phrase in response to three of the five open-ended questions. The residents' own suggestion of the need for training in clinical documentation, in response to question 11, is particularly interesting since many hospital administrators claim that residents, and physicians in general, have little or no interest in this type of training. The interest in training, coupled with the use of the key term "feedback," is also of interest. This suggests that the residents are interested not just in training on documentation; they want to apply what they have learned and receive constructive criticism on their work. The common phrases identified by question, and percentage of time used, can be found in figure 6.3.

USING RESPONSES TO THE QUESTIONNAIRE ABOUT ATTITUDES AND OPINIONS CONCERNING DOCUMENTATION

You should use the responses to the attitudes and opinions questionnaire to prepare for the training program and to guide your asking activities. The instructors for the clinical documentation study used the responses to the questionnaire to focus the asking process during training. The attitudes and opinions questionnaire asks the physicians for input on three groups of questions. These questions probe their beliefs about: (1) the impact of their own documentation, (2) the impact of documentation in general, and (3) the value of any prior training they had in clinical documentation. In general, the responses are rated on a verbal scale from "not at all" (or no value) to "a great deal." These verbal tags translate into a numerical scale that ranges from 0 to 4. The overall mean for attitudes and opinions was 3.1. The highest means were for rating of the statements (1) "documentation is important" and (2) "feedback on documentation is helpful." Both of these statements had a mean response of 3.77. The lowest mean score was for the statement "there is a relationship between the documentation I provide on a patient's hospital records and that patient's office records." The mean score for this statement was 1.63, with most trainees selecting *not sure* as their response.

The instructors were particularly interested in questions that had mean scores of 2.5 or less. In addition to the statement about hospital and office documentation noted above, there were three statements with mean scores at or below 2.5. These were: (1) "I believe my clinical documentation in a patient's record impacts research" (mean = 2.50); (2) "Good documentation should be acknowledged publicly" (mean = 2.13); and (3) "Dictating progress notes results in improved clinical documentation" (mean = 2.00). In addition, with the exception of training in medical school, the trainees rated their training in clinical documentation from other sources as either "none" or "poor." Some of the low scores on this questionnaire can be used to help an organization shape its ongoing clinical documentation program. For example, for this hospital, since the great majority of physicians do not believe good clinical documentation should be acknowledged publicly, the organization should use this information in designing reward and acknowledgement programs for physicians. (See figures 6.4–6.8.)

Figure 6.7 outlines the first two-hour educational program for CAMP Method training. The areas highlighted in gray reflect activities that involve asking components.

Figure 6.8 outlines the second two-hour educational program for CAMP Method training. Areas highlighted in gray reflect activities that contain asking components in the program. There are several areas that can overlap with asking, like coaching and peer learning. The instructor should take every opportunity possible to use as many of the CAMP Method components during training. This will result in stronger self-efficacy, which in turn will produce superior documentation results.

CHAPTER SUMMARY

The asking component of the CAMP Method for training involves soliciting feedback from physician training participants in a specific manner and at a specific time. The ability of physicians to openly speak their concerns about what they are being asked to do is essential. This differs from coaching because instead of addressing their ability to improve their clinical documentation, it addresses their willingness to do it. Physicians need to feel that their clinical documentation is not a forced process,

Figure 6.4. Questionnaire on Documentation

9. I believe that my clinical documentation in a patient's hospital record impacts:	Not at all	Very little	Not sure	Somewhat	A great deal
a. The patient's quality of care overall					
b. My medical malpractice exposure					
c. My "report card" or other public data profiles that detail my medical practices					
d. Medicare Quality Indicators					
e. Joint Commission (JCAHO) accreditation					
f. The treatment the patient receives from other caregivers					
g. Healthcare planning					
h. The follow-up care received by the patient					
i. Medical research					
j. Healthcare policy decisions					
k. Quality improvement projects					
l. The payment the hospital receives for the care delivered					
m. The payment I receive for the care delivered					

10. I believe that:	Definitely disagree	Disagree somewhat	Not sure	Agree somewhat	Definitely agree
a. Clinical documentation is important					
b. It is important for physicians to support the hospital's needs					
c. There is a relationship between the documentation I provide on a patient's hospital records and the patient's office records					
d. The government's role in healthcare is necessary					

	Definitely disagree	Disagree somewhat	Not sure	Agree somewhat	Definitely agree
e. Healthcare providers should comply with government regulations					
f. Feedback about documentation practices is helpful					
g. The use of templates improves clinical documentation					
h. Good documentation should be recognized via monetary rewards					
i. Good documentation should be acknowledged publicly					
j. The opinions of medical staff leaders impacts physician behavior					
k. It is important to have a positive hospital–physician relationship					
l. The use of an electronic patient record results in improved documentation in the patient's record					
m. Dictating progress notes results in improved documentation					
n. The use of checklists improves clinical documentation					

Figure 6.5. Experiences with Clinical Documentation

11. Please rate the value of the clinical documentation training you received from the following sources. If you did not receive any training from a listed source, check the box that corresponds to "none."	None	Poor	Below Average	Average	Above Average	Excellent
a. Medical school						
b. Prior residency programs						
c. The AMA						
d. A formal documentation improvement program						
e. The Internet						
f. Videotapes						
g. Audiotapes						
h. The hospital's compliance officer						
i. The hospital's HIM/medical record department						
j. Seminars I have attended						
k. The hospital's clinical documentation staff						

Figure 6.6. Other Questions About Clinical Documentation Practices on the Attitudes and Opinions Questionnaire

12. I have (check all that apply):

- ❑ Used an electronic patient record
- ❑ Used a PDA (personal digital assistant) to record clinical documentation
- ❑ Received feedback about my clinical documentation practices
- ❑ Used documentation templates to record my documentation in a patient's record
- ❑ Used checklists to record my documentation in a patient's record
- ❑ Had documentation audits on my clinical documentation by the hospital staff
- ❑ Had my documentation practices compared with my peers (profiles or report cards)
- ❑ Taken tests to determine my documentation proficiency
- ❑ Been penalized for poor documentation practices
- ❑ Been acknowledged for good documentation practices
- ❑ Received financial rewards for good documentation practices
- ❑ Learned about the latest developments in medical technology
- ❑ Dictated my progress notes for a patient's inpatient records

17. My most recent documentation training was within the last:

- ❑ week
- ❑ month
- ❑ year
- ❑ more than a year
- ❑ never

18. Have you ever received an inquiry to clarify your documentation in an inpatient medical record?

- ❑ Yes

Specify type of inquiry_____

- ❑ No

19. Overall, how would you rate the quality of your clinical documentation?

❑ Poor   ❑ Fair   ❑ Good   ❑ Very Good   ❑ Excellent

Figure 6.7. Course Contents of the First Two-hour Educational Program for CAMP Method Training Highlighting Activities that Involve Asking Questions

Construct	Activity	Program Design to Foster Construct	Time
Peer learning and coaching	Introduction	Review session outline and objectives. Physician instructor shares own experience with clinical documentation and assures participants that, with the appropriate training and support, they will master this process.	10 min
Mastering	Self-assessment and test	Participants take the self-assessment and the pre-test. Collect the self-assessment and the pre-test from the participants before reviewing the responses.	10 min
Peer learning	Test review	Review test questions and correct responses with attendees.	10 min
Asking	Resident commitment to good clinical documentation	Discuss the relationship between good documentation practices and improved patient outcomes with the participants. Ask physicians to share their concerns about clinical documentation. Make a list of what they are and share the list (as a way to end this portion of the session). State that we will revisit the list in the second session. Include time management if not addressed by physicians.	10 min
Peer learning	Documentation rules	Review documentation "rules" PowerPoint with physicians. Ask for and allow questions throughout this portion of the presentation.	15 min
Asking	Break	Serve refreshments and take a 5-minute break.	10 min
Peer learning and mastering	Case study examples	Review cases studies 1–5 that correspond with objectives 2–5.	15 min
Mastering	Tools	Provide each physician with a *Clinical Documentation Improvement Handbook* and a *Doc Pocket Tool*. Review the contents of the handbook and the tool. Allow for questions throughout this portion of the presentation.	15 min
Mastering and asking	Case study exercises	Give physicians case study exercises 1–5 that contain documentation from actual patient records to review and provide the correct documentation to identify the patient's diagnosis/es. Review answers with physicians asking participants for their responses. Provide feedback as each participant shares his answers.	15 min
Asking	MD concerns	Revisit list of concerns from beginning of the program.	10 min
Coaching	Conclusion	Conclude the program by assuring the physicians that they can document well. Ask them to apply the concepts they have learned between now and the next session, and be prepared to share their experiences during the next session.	5 min

Figure 6.8. Contents of the Second Two-hour Educational Program for CAMP Method Training Highlighting Activities that Involve Asking Questions

Construct	Activity	Program Design to Foster Construct	Time
Coaching	Introduction	Review session outline and objectives. Return the pre-test results to each participant. Physician instructor asks participants to share their documentation experiences over the past week. Provide feedback to examples.	15 min
Peer learning and coaching	DVD viewing	Have attendees view DVD of physicians discussing their concerns about documentation. At the completion of the video ask physicians to share their opinions of the documentation concepts shared in the DVD.	20 min
Mastering and coaching	Case study examples	Review cases studies 6–10 that correspond with objectives 1–6. Ask participants to comment on the examples. Provide feedback on comments.	15 min
Asking	Break	Serve refreshments and take a 5-minute break allowing participants to interact with each other.	10 min
Mastering and coaching	Case study exercises	Give physicians case study exercises 6–10 that contain documentation from actual patient records to review and provide the correct documentation to identify the patients' diagnoses. Review answers with physicians asking participants for their responses. Provide feedback as each participant shares answers.	15 min
Mastering, peer learning, coaching, and asking	Tools	Ask physicians to refer to their *Clinical Documentation Implementation Handbook* and *Doc Pocket Tool*. Ask participants to provide examples of where and when they were able to use either tool over the past week (since the first session). Provide feedback on the use of the tools as shared by the participants. Use any remaining time to review the contents of the book again.	15 min
Asking	Resident commitment	Review listing of concerns generated by residents during previous session. Identify how their dedication and commitment to medicine can be demonstrated through good documentation practices. Ask the residents to sign a "Commitment to Improved Clinical Documentation form."	10 min
	Post-test	Have participants take the self-assessment and the post-test. Collect the self-assessments and the post-tests. Review the answers with the participants.	15 min
Coaching	Conclusion	Conclude the program by assuring the physicians that they can document well.	5 min
Asking	Evaluation	Ask participants to evaluate the educational program.	2 min

but rather something they control. It is best if the physician instructor leads the asking process during the training session since the trainees are likely to relate well to him. However, the instructor team needs to be prepared with appropriate responses to manage the discussion so that physicians feel comfortable with the response and the group can move through the training session without significant interruption. A good way to prepare for complaints from physicians is to study their responses on the attitudes and opinions questionnaire.

STEPS YOU CAN TAKE TODAY

- If your organization does not ask physicians about their concerns with what they are being asked to do during a clinical documentation training session, discuss the reasons with your colleagues. Determine a way to pull the asking component into your training for this program.
- Ask a few physicians to complete the attitudes and opinions questionnaire and discuss their responses with them. Are there any concerns that you can act on today (or this week) to make an improvement that will impact them positively?

7. Optimal Training Schedule and Time Management for Physicians

THE CAMP METHOD study uses an optimal training schedule for physician clinical documentation training. The training process involves classroom sessions delivered on either side of practicing the skill. It is important for both quality and compliance purposes that physicians have the time to learn clinical documentation practices correctly. This means the physicians participate in four total hours of instruction and apply the concepts introduced to them between sessions. Most clinical documentation training is limited in scope and time. And as the study results show, even a limited 90-minute training program produces suboptimal results. In the end, it is the healthcare organization's responsibility to provide *effective* training to their medical staff on clinical documentation issues.

In the clinical documentation study, time management was identified by physicians as the largest, most commonly perceived barrier to high quality clinical documentation. After initial training and practice, many physicians reconsidered their concerns. However, because time management is a significant up-front concern for most physicians, it will be helpful for your organization to acknowledge this and provide some relief to physicians. More importantly, because lack of time is consistently identified by physicians as a significant concern regarding their clinical documentation, it is important for the instructors to be familiar with time management principles and, in particular, how those principles have been applied to physicians. This chapter describes some options for helping physicians with time management objections.

WHO IS RESPONSIBLE FOR SCHEDULING?

It is necessary to identify one individual in your organization who is responsible for scheduling physician training and coordinating all of the related activities. Centralized scheduling accomplishes some key points. First, it ensures that the training sessions actually get launched. Second, centralized scheduling ensures that there are no conflicts or overlaps in training sessions. And finally, centralized scheduling increases accountability for both the organization and the physician trainees. Just having one person who people can reach out to with questions and who everyone knows will track you down if you miss a session increases accountability. In large organizations, at least one backup person should be identified.

WHY WILL THE PHYSICIANS COME?

Two things are necessary to get physicians to show up for a training session: a sense of urgency created by your organization and the physicians' own desire to learn. First, the organization must make the cause an important one. Clinical documentation must be an inherent part of the organization's mission and the physicians must understand how the two relate to one another. You can find a detailed description of the role clinical documentation plays in strategy development in volume 1 of this book. Second, the physician must have a desire to participate in the education. There can be many ways to increase a physician's willingness to participate in a training program. In some cases, the fact that the issue is an urgent one for the physician is enough. But in most cases, you will need to put many plans into motion in order to ensure attendance at clinical documentation training sessions. Some of the things that impact attendance may include the following. The more of these points that you include in your planning process, the better your attendance and participation is likely to be:

- In communications about the training program, clearly state how the program furthers the organization's mission and vision.
- Consider making the sessions mandatory.

- Plan sessions around breakfast, lunch, or dinner.
- Dedicate the training time to clinical documentation only; do not add it as an agenda item to some other meeting. Doing so decreases the importance of the activity.
- Offer continuing education credits.
- Have a special guest speaker provide the introduction.

HOW WILL IT BE COMMUNICATED?

How the training is communicated to physicians is as important as the training itself. If not communicated properly, physicians will not attend, and the organization's purpose will not be fulfilled. You should develop a specific methodology for the types and numbers of communications and announcements. But you should also determine who the communications should be from. Many organizations enlist the help of the CEO to promote the training through an initial letter. Then they follow up with an e-mail from the director of the service that references the CEO's letter. Every organization is different in terms of what will carry weight and get the physicians' attention. Determine what will work best for your physicians by getting their feedback before investing in a specific communications strategy. Some suggestions for how you can communicate the message are noted below:

- Create brochures, posters, and other marketing materials for the training just like any other concept or activity you are trying to sell.
- Send out announcements to physicians individually using a multitiered strategy. For example, send a general e-mail, an e-mail from the physician's chief of service, a hard copy letter from the CEO, and possibly even a fax announcement.
- Require an RSVP.
- Send an acknowledgement of the RSVP.
- Call or send a reminder about the training sessions the day prior to the session.

Figure 7.1. Training Activities

Activity	Comments
Physician takes pre-test and completes questionnaires	The most efficient way to have your physicians complete the pre-test and pre-session questionnaires (self-efficacy and attitudes and opinions) is to have them complete the questionnaires online using the CAMP Method Web site. Your subscription to the Web site provides a tracking mechanism for pre- and post-test results. It also provides you with an analysis of questionnaire results with areas for suggested focus during the asking and coaching sections of the training.
Analysis of pre-tests and questionnaires	You and your training team should analyze test and questionnaire results prior to training. You can do this manually or use the CAMP Method Web site.
Session 1	Session 1 is conducted ideally during one 2-hour time period. If physicians are unable to be available for a full two hours, then two 1-hour sessions can be used, but are likely to result in a 2 to 3 point differential in post-test scores.
Intersession activities	At the end of training session 1, physicians are provided with tools and specific instructions for their intersession observation of clinical documentation activities—both their own and their peers' documentation. They should come prepared to session 2 to share their experiences with the group. This intersession activity ideally should occur for no less than 7 days and no more than 10 days.
Session 2	Session 2 is ideally conducted during one 2-hour time period. If physicians are unable to be available for a full 2 hours, then two 1-hour sessions can be used, but are likely to result in a 2–3 point differential in post-test scores.
Post-test and questionnaires	Physicians complete a post-test (the same instrument they completed as the pre-test), another self-efficacy questionnaire, and a program evaluation. All of the tests and questionnaires can be completed online using the CAMP Method Web site subscription.

WHAT'S THE PLAN?: CREATE A CHECKLIST OF ALL ACTIVITIES THAT NEED TO BE COVERED IN TRAINING

Once the physicians have registered for the training, you need to kick off the presession activities. The training process contains mandatory activities to ensure your organization will benefit from the CAMP™ Method training. These specific activities are listed in figure 7.1 with a few comments about how they should be implemented. The resource disc contains a sample checklist.

TIME MANAGEMENT

During the clinical documentation study, physician participants noted on both the self-efficacy questionnaire and the attitudes and opinions survey that their biggest concern about their ability to provide high quality clinical documentation in a patient's record was lack of time. Time was also discussed during the *asking* activities of both training sessions. Most physicians today find their time is being reprioritized for them. For example, the average insurance company assumes that an initial primary care visit will take 16 minutes, while a follow-up visit should take anywhere from 6 to 8 minutes at most.[1] With these kinds of demands placed on their time, physicians are likely to feel significant stress about time management. As a result, you may want to address time management in a subtle but useful way with the physicians who are to participate in your training groups.

There are many time management strategies and books written in general about time management. Anyone can learn from these resources. But if you are going to make suggestions or provide resources to your physicians, it is important that you provide resources that are relevant for physicians. Using the CAMP Method encourages physicians to accept, internalize, and act on the information. Ideally, if you can provide a short time management session for physicians *before* the clinical documentation training begins, it will be more likely to make an impact on the attendees. You can offer time management sessions live and over the Internet. Either way, it is important to get useful information about time management into the hands of your medical staff, in the easiest and most convenient manner for your physicians.

PHYSICIAN TIME MANAGEMENT AND SELF-EFFICACY

Supporting your physicians in the time management process can result in better clinical documentation practices. Individuals with training in self-efficacy report less physical and psychological strain with long work hours, and work overload, compared to individuals without self-efficacy training or with low self-efficacy.[2] Time management training can also help an individual feel more effective and in control of his life. The CAMP Method training for clinical documentation can help physicians deal with the stress of clinical documentation demands. To the extent that your organization can provide resources in both areas, your physicians are likely to be more productive, cooperative, and satisfied.

In *De-Stressing Doctors: A Self-Management Guide*, Sutherland and

Cooper state that hospital demands, patient expectations, insurance company and reimbursement challenges, and the need to keep abreast of medical and technological developments add to the workload of physicians.[3] They describe the following three elements of a time management system: (1) goal setting and prioritization, (2) mechanics, like making lists and preparing for work, and (3) having a systematic approach to work, including delegation and avoiding interruptions. Most time management methods have these three elements in common. While physicians need to set their own goals, the organization can make the time management process easier for the physician by being clear about what its priorities are.

You communicate your priorities in your organization's vision and mission. But applying the vision and mission statements in a meaningful way to the high priority work you have for physicians can help them prioritize their own work. The organization needs to be clear that high quality clinical documentation matters, and that it is the physician's ultimate responsibility to provide high quality clinical documentation in every patient record. The organization provides guidance and support in the clinical documentation process; but ultimately, it is the physician's responsibility to follow through. Steven Covey's work in *7 Habits of Highly Effective People* further supports this concept. Covey's third habit, *First Things First* (also a separate book on this principle), is the culmination of habits one (be proactive) and two (begin with the end in mind, or have a vision). Habit three is the day-to-day *performing* of habits one and two. Covey further claims that without being proactive and without having a vision, you cannot effectively implement any goal, whether it be improving the quality of clinical documentation or managing your time more effectively. In other words, you will not be able to effectively manage your time unless you are proactive and know where you are going.[4]

TIME MANAGEMENT FOR PHYSICIANS: WHAT ELSE CAN YOU DO?

There are a few noted authors and experts on time management, and among them are Julie Morgenstern and Alec Mackenzie. Both have written books listing things we can all do to increase our efficiency and decrease the things that make us inefficient.

Julie Morgenstern wrote *Never Check E-mail in the Morning* and Alec Mackenzie wrote *The Time Trap: The Classic Book on Time Management*. Some of the suggestions Morgenstern makes that can be used by anyone who is trying to be more in control of her time include:

1. Choose the most important tasks
2. Create the time to get things done
3. Control the nibblers
4. Organize at the speed of change
5. Master delegation

Other suggestions Morgenstern makes are listed below; these could be helpful to physicians if delivered by another physician, or person they respect and believe is knowledgeable on the subject:

1. Embrace your work/life balance
2. Develop an entrepreneurial mindset
3. Work well with others
4. Leverage your value[5]

In *The Time Trap*, Alec Mackenzie describes the 20 biggest time wasters and how to cure them. Some of the top time wasters not already mentioned in Morgenstern's book, that could be useful to physicians, include:

1. The inability to say no: say no firmly, give reasons, and offer alternatives
2. Paperwork: handle, delegate, file, and expedite
3. Poor communication: listen, clarify, and ask for feedback
4. Travel: use travel time to get things done[6]

In *The Time Trap*, Mackenzie shares the time management techniques of Dr. Julia Files, a physician from the Mayo Clinic. Dr. Files talks about "running a minute by minute schedule, not an hour by hour schedule" and approaching tasks in small increments. She also practices focused concentration to attend to the task at hand. Dr. Files uses car and shower time to plan.[7] These kinds of examples, which highlight other physicians' stories about how they effectively manage time, are particularly helpful for physicians to hear.

In "Ten Time-Management Tips for Family Practice Physicians," published in the *Canadian Medical Association Journal*, Dr. John Crosby describes some of his own successful time management strategies. First among them is to *get help*. Crosby suggests physicians set up mutually convenient, paid, three-hour long, uninterrupted Saturday morning meetings to brainstorm about how time is wasted in your office. Like Dr. Files, Crosby suggests *doing things in batches, minimizing interruptions, and multitasking*. For paperwork, he suggests doing it daily and only touching paper one time. He also recommends using *advice sheets* for common acute and chronic conditions.[8] These sheets can be given to the patient or referenced by the physician.

Another article, "Life Balance: 17 Tips from Doctors, for Doctors," written by Jennifer Bush for the American Academy of Family Practice, surveyed physicians to identify some of their best time management strategies. Among them are the following words of wisdom, from doctors to doctors: Don't try to be too efficient. Take time to really listen to a couple of patient stories a day; we need to be fed by our patients. Learn when to multitask and when to focus wholeheartedly on things that deserve your full attention. Develop a support system, and realize that each one of us has our own mountain to climb. Try to remember to pause to enjoy the view along the way and to help and let yourself be helped by others you meet on the path.[9]

You may want to consider making time management resources available to your medical staff, including the books and articles cited above.

SURVEY YOUR PHYSICIANS ABOUT THEIR OWN SUCCESSES WITH TIME MANAGEMENT CHALLENGES

One of the principles demonstrated by the CAMP Method is that physicians learn better from other physicians whom they respect. Every medical staff is full of physicians who have accomplishments outside of the practice of medicine. Chances are great that you have a few who have mastered the art of time management. Seek out these physicians. If you find one, ask if she is willing to share her success with her peers in a brief training session. You can also write an article about her management process in a newsletter or other publication that your physicians read. If you have more than one physician who has mastered time management, perhaps these physicians can conduct a panel discussion and invite the entire medical staff to attend. The more physicians you can identify and involve in the process, the more likely others will be to attend a session.

CHAPTER SUMMARY

Organization and time management are important components of the training process. An optimal training schedule was used in the CAMP Method study to develop self-efficacy. The closer you stay to the original schedule, the more likely you are to produce highly effective results for your organization. Physicians have identified that the lack of time for training and documenting is a significant concern. To keep your clinical documentation training on track, address time management issues with physicians before the clinical documentation sessions begin. The physician leaders in your organization can share stories of how other physicians, like those mentioned in this chapter, have mastered time management challenges. Or, if you have physicians on your medical staff with personal time management success stories, ask them to share their stories with their peers.

STEPS YOU CAN TAKE TODAY

- Review the schedule of activities with your colleagues. Identify the support you need in your organization in order to provide training using this schedule.
- Suggest that the executive team review volume 1 of this series to develop a better appreciation for the importance of clinical documentation training for your organization.
- Use some of the time management techniques recommended in this chapter to help you better manage the multiple demands of the clinical documentation process.

8. Using the Tools

T HE TRAINING TOOLS provided in this volume are the exact training materials used in the CAMP™ Method study. If you conduct the training consistent with the steps described in this book, which mirror the study, you should expect to see a significant improvement in the quality of the clinical documentation provided by your physicians. There are two types of tools used in the training program. The first are measurement tools used to measure physician skills, confidence, and beliefs. The second are training tools used by the instructors to teach the training program. This chapter describes both sets of tools.

Copies of each tool are provided in the appendix and on the resource disc that accompanies *A Compelling Case for Clinical Documentation*. The physician survey, questionnaire, and test can be administered in one of three ways. First, you can administer the tools manually and enter the responses into your own database or an SPSS-like database for analysis. Second, you can load the information onto your organization's learning management system and track responses and results through the system. Third, you can subscribe to the CAMP Method survey system that physicians can access on the Web. If you use the CAMP Method survey system, you will have access to your organization's database and the CAMP Method-generated analytic reports.

MEASUREMENT TOOLS

Three measurement tools are used in the training program to measure physician skills, confidence, and beliefs. The results of the measurement tools are used by the instructors to fashion the initial training program to meet the specific needs of the physicians in the program; to appropriately focus the follow-up training; and as evidence of the knowledge base of physicians regarding clinical documentation for regulatory and compliance purposes.

Attitudes and Opinions Survey: a survey regarding the physicians' attitudes and opinions about clinical documentation is administered prior to the training program. The purpose of this survey is to see if physicians have concerns that can be addressed during the training. Physicians should feel comfortable with the educational process; and if the questionnaires tip you off that someone does not feel comfortable, you should address this during the presentation. In the end, one of your primary goals should be for physicians to own the task of clinical documentation—and to want to perform the task in a high quality manner. Negativity, and misconceptions about the process and expectations, can prevent you and the physicians from reaching this goal.

Self-Efficacy Questionnaire: a questionnaire to measure physicians' confidence regarding the quality of their own clinical documentation. This questionnaire is administered both before and after the training program. Self-efficacy is an essential component of the physicians' confidence that they can practice high quality clinical documentation and that this skill, once acquired, is sustainable.

Clinical Documentation Test: a test to measure what the physicians know and what they don't know about clinical documentation practices. This test is administered before and after the training program. The results of the pre-test are used to identify areas of concern or weakness that the instructors can focus on during the initial training session. The results of the post-test are used to identify specific follow-up training needs of the physicians.

TRAINING TOOLS

Training tools are tools used by the instructors. These tools are provided in the appendix and on the resource disc.

Agenda and schedule of training activities. The agenda and schedule of activities is a detailed listing of the topics that are addressed during the two training sessions. In addition to the topics, this tool lists specific instructions and tips for the trainers. The tool also lists the amount of time that the instructor should spend presenting information in the topic area to the trainees.

PowerPoint training presentations. There are two PowerPoint presentations for the CAMP Method training program, one for each of the two training sessions. The resource disc contains two copies of each set of slides—one with answers and one without. The set of slides without answers is provided as a handout for session participants. The PowerPoint slides begin with session objectives. The slides follow the order of the agenda and address the six criteria for high quality clinical documentation and key topic areas. Practical application of the criteria and key topics are introduced first via case summaries and then via more detailed case studies. Each set of slides contains five one-page case summaries of clinical documentation that do not meet one or more criteria for quality.

Case studies. There are 10 case studies. These are provided as PDF files on the resource disc. The case studies contain, on average, six to eight pages of information from deidentified inpatient medical records. Forms in the case studies may be histories and physicals, progress notes, laboratory, radiology, or other ancillary reports, and discharge summaries. Using the case study information and the concepts learned in the program, physicians are asked to identify any documentation deficiencies in each case study and how they would document the entry differently. Physicians complete five case studies during the first session and five case studies during the second session.

Video clip. A seven-minute video clip is included on the resource disc. The video is a panel discussion of four physicians (actors playing a family practice physician, a cardiologist, an orthopedic surgeon, and a general surgeon) discussing clinical documentation concerns. The film provides a light-hearted break to the lecture and exercises, and it also acts as a good segue to additional group discussion.

Evaluation. The training evaluation forms are provided on the resource disc. Physicians can complete them manually or online. If the physicians complete the evaluations online at the CAMP Method site when they take the post-test and the post-training self-efficacy questionnaire, you will receive an analysis of the evaluation results along with the other CAMP Method reports.

RESULTS OF PHYSICIAN MEASUREMENT TOOLS

The following figures are examples of results from the test, survey, and questionnaires administered to study participants during the clinical documentation study that validated the CAMP Methodology. These results are provided not only to illustrate study findings, but also to show you examples of reports you can obtain from the CAMP Method Web site.

Results of Attitudes and Opinions Survey

The figures in this chapter illustrate the mean scores overall, by group of questions, and for questions 9, 10, and 11. The questionnaire responses were scored on a 5-point Likert scale from 0 to 4 with 0 = *Not at all*, 1 = *Very little*, 2 = *Not sure*, 3 = *Somewhat*, and 4 = *A great deal*. The mean score for clinical documentation in inpatient medical records attitudes and opinions questions was 2.93 for all groups. The range was 2.31, with a minimum of 1.69, maximum of 4.00, and standard deviation of .478. This information is broken down into control group, CAMP Method group, and limited training group results in figure 8.1.

When asked about their beliefs regarding the impact of clinical documentation practices overall, the mean response was 3.12. The range for responses to this question was 2.29 with a minimum of 1.64 and a maximum of 3.93, and standard deviation of .410. This information, broken out by study and control group, is illustrated in figure 8.2.

When asked to rate the quality of their previous exposure to clinical documentation training, the mean response overall was .5257. The wording scale used for this question was: 0 = *None (no exposure)*; 1 = *Poor*; 2 = *Below Average*; 3 = *Average*; 4 = *Above Average*; and 5 = *Excellent*. The control group mean was .6159. The CAMP Method group and limited training group means were .4667 and .4844 respectively. Prior to the program recruitment, it was determined that the residents had no prior inpatient clinical documentation training during their residency. This was revalidated through the demographic instrument. In fact, all

Figure 8.1. Importance of Residents' Own Clinical Documentation Attitudes and Opinions Measurement (Range = 0 to 4)

Measure	All Groups	Control Group	CAMP Method Group	Limited Training Group
Mean	2.93	2.95	2.95	2.90
N	91	31	30	30

Figure 8.2. Attitude About the Impact of Documentation in General (Range = 0 to 4)

Measure	All Groups	Control Group	CAMP Method Group	Limited Training Group
Mean	3.12	3.04	3.16	3.17
N	91	31	30	30

Figure 8.3. Study Participants' Prior Experiences with Clinical Documentation Training (Range = 0 to 4)

Measure	All Groups	Control Group	CAMP Method Group	Limited Training Group
Mean	.5257	.6159	.4667	.4944
N	91	31	30	30

of the findings were within the range of 0 (none) and 1 (poor rating). This indicated that the study participants had very minimal exposure, if any, to previous inpatient clinical documentation training. The mean results for question 11, by group, can be found in figure 8.3.

It is interesting to note that of the three questions about clinical documentation attitudes and opinions, the highest overall mean score, 3.12, was for question 10 (beliefs about clinical documentation in general). The mean score for question nine (beliefs about the impact of the resident's own documentation) was not far behind at 2.97. However, there is a stark difference between these two attitudes questions and the responses to question 11 on clinical documentation training exposures. The mean of .5257 suggests that residents believe that documentation is important, but they received little to no training to prepare them to practice quality documentation in the hospital setting. A more detailed analysis of the specific questions within each section of the attitudes and opinions questionnaire follows.

Figure 8.4. Responses to Question 9: Means by Group (Range = 0 to 4)

Question 9: I believe that my clinical documentation in a patient's hospital record impacts the following:	CAMP Method Group	Limited Training Group	Control Group	All Groups
The patient's quality of care overall	3.33	3.40	3.29	3.34
My medical malpractice exposure	3.60	3.33	3.45	3.46
My "report card" / public data profiles that detail medical practices	2.60	2.67	2.84	2.70
Medicare Quality Indicators	3.27	3.17	3.23	3.22
The Joint Commission (JCAHO) accreditation	3.30	3.27	3.52	3.36
The treatment the patient receives from other caregivers	3.13	3.50	3.52	3.38
Healthcare planning	3.00	3.13	2.87	3.00
The follow-up care received by the patient	3.03	3.27	2.87	3.05
Medical research	2.50	2.37	2.61	2.49
Healthcare policy decisions	2.20	2.13	2.32	2.22
Quality improvement projects	3.10	2.87	3.00	2.99
The payment the hospital receives for the care delivered	3.63	3.45	3.42	3.50
The payment I receive for the care delivered	1.63	.93	1.35	1.31
Overall mean score for question 9	2.95	2.88	2.95	2.93

Figure 8.4 lists each subquestion in question nine along with the corresponding mean response by group. Of particular interest here is the fact that the highest mean scores came in response to residents' beliefs that their documentation impacted quality of care and that their documentation impacted their medical malpractice exposure. These means were 3.46 and 3.34 respectively. The lowest overall mean score, 1.31, reflects residents' beliefs that their documentation impacts the payment they receive for the care delivered to the patient. It is true in clinical practice that there is no relationship between a resident's salary and his documentation. However, once the residents complete their residency programs, there will be a relationship between documentation and payment they receive in their clinical practice of medicine.

Figure 8.5 is a listing of all of the sub-questions contained in question 10. The three highest means came in response to the first question in

Figure 8.5. Responses to Question 10: Means by Group (Range = 0 to 4)

Question 10: I believe that ...	CAMP Method Group	Limited Training Group	Control Group	All Groups
Clinical documentation is important	3.77	3.80	3.74	3.77
It is important for physicians to support the hospital's needs	3.28	3.33	3.42	3.34
There is a relationship between the documentation I provide on a patient's hospital record and that patient's office record	2.93	2.70	2.87	2.84
The government's role in healthcare is necessary	3.27	3.23	2.87	3.12
Healthcare providers should comply with government regulations	3.40	3.27	3.10	3.25
Feedback about documentation practices is helpful	3.77	3.57	3.52	3.62
The use of templates improves clinical documentation	3.70	3.47	3.23	3.46
Good documentation should be recognized via monetary rewards	2.53	2.60	2.71	2.62
Good documentation should be acknowledged publicly	2.13	2.60	2.03	2.25
The opinions of medical staff leaders impact physician behavior	3.10	3.23	3.00	3.11
It is important to have a positive hospital–physician relationship	3.73	3.80	3.77	3.77
The use of an EMR results in improved documentation	3.62	3.50	3.23	3.44
Dictating progress notes results in improved documentation	2.00	2.10	2.23	2.11
The use of checklists improves clinical documentation	3.10	3.17	2.84	3.03
Overall mean score for question 10	3.16	3.17	3.04	3.12

this section, in which the residents were asked to rate the importance of clinical documentation. The mean response for this question was 3.77. In addition, when the residents were asked to rate the importance of a positive hospital–physician relationship, the mean response was 3.77. The mean response for the question asking the residents to rate the value of feedback regarding their clinical documentation was 3.62. The lowest rating, 2.11, was in response to whether dictation would

Figure 8.6. Responses to Question 11: Means by Group (Range = 0 to 4)

Question 11: Please rate the value of clinical documentation training you received from the following sources.	CAMP Method Group	Limited Training Group	Control Group	All Groups
Medical school	2.63	3.07	2.35	2.68
Prior residency programs	.60	.52	.93	.69
The American Medical Association	.03	.00	.16	.07
A formal documentation improvement program	.30	.50	.45	.42
The Internet	.10	.10	.13	.11
Videotapes	.00	.00	.00	.00
Audiotapes	.00	.00	.00	.00
The hospital's compliance officer	.60	.17	.65	.47
The hospital's HIM/medical records department	.20	.37	.90	.49
Seminars I have attended	.20	.23	.71	.38
The hospital's clinical documentation staff	.40	.27	1.10	.59
Total mean score for question 11	.47	.49	.62	.53

result in higher quality clinical documentation. Other low means were for "good documentation should be acknowledged publicly" (2.25) and "good documentation should be recognized via monetary rewards" (2.62). This last rating is interesting, especially in light of the fact that when the residents responded in the discussion about their concerns regarding clinical documentation, many stated that there was no monetary incentive for them to focus on high quality clinical documentation.

Figure 8.6 is a listing of all of the specific questions contained in question 11 about the value of the residents' prior training in clinical documentation. As noted previously, with the exception of the education they received in medical school, these scores were all less than one. This further reinforces the fact that the residents did not have prior exposure to clinical documentation training. All values were zero for questions about any education received through the videotapes and audiotapes. Other low mean scores (less than .50) came in response to questions concerning any education received through the American Medical Association, the Internet, the hospital's compliance officer,

Figure 8.7. Pre- and Post-test Self-Efficacy Mean Ratings by Group

Group		Self-Efficacy Overall Preintervention	Self-Efficacy Overall Postintervention	Variance
CAMP Method Group	Mean	2.6702	2.8872	+.217
	Standard deviation	.38477	.51996	
Limited Training Group	Mean	2.7259	2.8007	+.0748
	Standard deviation	.37359	.36026	
Control Group	Mean	2.8122	2.7884	–.0238
	Standard deviation	.47893	.44396	
Total	Mean	2.7369	2.8250	+.0881
	Standard deviation	.41547	.44338	

the hospital's Health Information Management (HIM) department, a formal documentation program, or seminars.

Results of Self-Efficacy Questionnaire

The first and last question on the self-efficacy questionnaire asked the participants to rate the quality of their clinical documentation by checking the description that best reflected their feelings about their documentation: Poor, Fair, Good, Very Good, and Excellent. Then, each of these responses was coded—*Poor* = 0, *Fair* = 1, *Good* = 2, *Very Good* = 3, or *Excellent* = 4—to allow for a calculation of mean responses. The highest difference in mean scores by group was for the CAMP Method training group. The change in mean from pre- to post-test was as high as .25 for the CAMP Method training group. However, the differences in mean scores for the limited training group and the control group was as low as zero and as high as .22.

Figure 8.7 lists the overall pre- and post-test self-efficacy mean ratings by group. The mean scores overall were 2.74 to 2.83 with a mean change of +.088. Of most interest is the fact that the overall mean of the CAMP Method training group, the group with four constructs of self-efficacy embedded in the training session, increased .217 from pre-test to post-test. The overall mean of the limited training group, the group with exposure to two of the four constructs of self-efficacy, increased .075 from pre- to post-test. Finally, the overall mean of the control group decreased (–.024) from the pre- to post-test time period. These means offer preliminary evidence that self-efficacy increases as a result of clinical documentation training, as stated in hypotheses numbers two and four.

In addition to a basic analysis of the overall results of the self-efficacy questionnaire, the next nine tables provide a more in-depth analysis of the change in means from the pre-test to post-test time period for each section of the self-efficacy questionnaire. In some cases, the tables represent specific questions. In others, where the questions are very similar in nature (like questions three and four) they are combined into one table.

Figure 8.8 shows the mean changes for all of the sections of question two in the self-efficacy questionnaire. The overall total mean differences noted on the last row of the table support the hypotheses in general and show the most significant mean differences for the CAMP Method group (+.77), followed by the limited training group (+.48), and the control group (–.31). Of particular note is the consistent negative finding for confidence in documenting all of the patient's acute conditions.

Figure 8.9 shows the difference in means by group for questions three and four on the self-efficacy questionnaire. The overall means support the proposed hypotheses. The CAMP Method group had the highest mean difference (+1.99), the limited training group had the next highest mean difference (+.44), and the control group showed a variance of +.08. Of particular note was the fact that while the CAMP Method group showed the highest mean differences, there were negative variances for three specific subquestions. These questions, along with their negative variances, concerned confidence in documenting: (1) etiology of chest pain (–.06); (2) etiology of abdominal pain (–.06); and (3) etiology of shortness of breath (–.07). The limited training group also had negative variances in two of these three areas.

These unexpected negative variance findings in the intervention

Figure 8.8. Differences in Means Before and After Intervention—Self-Efficacy Question 2

Confidence in documenting . . .	CAMP Method Group	Limited Training Group	Control Group	All Groups
Legibly	+.10	+.10	−.13	+.03
All of the patient's chronic conditions	−.07	+.06	−.03	−.02
All of the patient's acute conditions	−.14	−.09	−.06	−.10
The clinical significance of an abnormal diagnostic test	+.27	+.10	+.13	+.17
Patient's diagnoses on radiology reports	+.04	+.06	−.14	+.05
Patient's diagnoses on pathology reports	+.24	+.23	−.07	+.13
Patient's diagnoses in the progress notes prior to discharge	+.03	−.03	.03	−.01
Discharge summary	+.24	+.03	+.07	+.11
Overall confidence in documenting these concepts	+.06	+.02	−.053	+.001
Total	+.77	.+.48	−.31	+.36

groups highlight two issues. First, this may represent an area for future development of the training program. Second, and more importantly, because the control group scored positively on these questions, lack of training in the control group may have resulted in a false positive result. In essence, because all residents have so little exposure to clinical documentation training, as evidenced in the attitudes and opinions questionnaire, it may be that the residents are not aware of what they do not know and, therefore, erroneously rate themselves higher on the self-efficacy questionnaire.

Figure 8.10 lists the mean differences by group for all of the subquestions in question five of the self-efficacy questionnaire. The CAMP Method group has the highest mean difference from pre- to post-test of +1.79. The limited training group has the next highest mean difference of +1.16. And the control group shows a negative mean variance of −.27. There are no surprising results in the individual questions.

DOCUMENTATION TEST RESULTS

This section discusses the basic statistical findings generated from the test scores. These data were analyzed in two ways. First, the data were analyzed by all groups together and then by each study and control group. Second, the data were analyzed by subsections of the test. These sections were broken out as the multiple choice section and the written response section. The breakout was determined based upon the similarity of test questions. Overall, each group's scores were higher for the multiple choice section of the test. There could be several reasons for this. First, the multiple choice questions addressed more basic information about clinical documentation. Second, because they were multiple choice, there was no penalty for guessing at the right question. Figure 8.11 shows the mean scores and other descriptive statistics for all study participants. The mean total test score for all groups before any intervention was .6726; the mean total test score after the interventions was .8332. Test results broken out by group appear in the figures 8.12–8.15.

Figure 8.12 shows the pre- and post-test scores, before and after training, for the CAMP Method group. After the intervention, the total score changed from 68 percent to 95 percent, an increase of 25 percentage points. In addition, it is worth noting that there was less variation in the scores after the intervention. Variances prior to intervention were .03, .02, and .02. After intervention variances were .002, .005, and .002.

Figure 8.13 shows the pre- and post-test scores before and after intervention for the limited training group. After the intervention, the score changed from 68 to 88 percent, an increase of 20 percentage points. Like the CAMP Method group, the variance in score was reduced after the intervention. Variances for the limited training group prior to intervention were .03, .02, and .02. After intervention variances were .012, .009, and .008.

Figure 8.14 shows the pre- and post-test scores for the control group. As noted previously, the control group received no intervention. Therefore, unless the study group contaminated a control group member, we would expect to see no improvement in test scores. In this case, there was essentially no improvement in scores, which supports

Figure 8.9. Difference in Means Before and After Intervention—Self-Efficacy Questions 3 and 4

Confidence in documenting . . .	CAMP Method Group	Limited Training Group	Control Group	All Groups
Etiology of chest pain	−.06	−.08	0	+.05
Etiology of abdominal pain	−.06	+.03	+.03	0
Etiology of shortness of breath	−.07	−.18	+.03	−.07
Etiology of syncope	+.13	+.10	−.03	+.07
Etiology of vertigo	+.33	+.15	−.10	+.12
Clinical significance of abnormal labs	+.23	+.10	0	+.11
Clinical significance of abnormal EKGs	+.33	+.03	+.03	+.13
Clinical significance of abnormal X-rays	+.37	0	−.07	+.10
Clinical significance of abnormal CT scan	+.36	+.13	+.06	+.19
Clinical significance of abnormal culture and sensitivity	+.30	+.16	+.10	+.12
Clinical significance of abnormal echocardiogram	+.13	0	+.03	+.06
Total differences in means	+1.99	+.44	+.08	+.88

Figure 8.10. Differences in Means Before and After Intervention—Self-Efficacy Question 5

Confidence in documenting . . .	CAMP Method Group	Limited Training Group	Control Group	All Groups
So the coder can accurately code	+.63	+.30	0	+.31
To meet Medicare requirements	+.60	+.43	−.17	+.29
To meet the Joint Commission requirements	+.56	+.43	−.10	+.30
Total differences in means	+1.79	+1.16	−.27	+.90

Figure 8.11. Pre- and Post-test Scores for All Groups

		Pre-test scores in multiple choice section	Pre-test scores in written section	Total pre-test scores	Post-test scores in written section	Post-test scores in multiple choice section	Total post-test scores
N	Valid	91	91	91	91	91	91
	Missing	0	0	0	0	0	0
Mean		.8095	.6128	.6726	.8052	.8974	.8332
Median		.8333	.6364	.6835	.8545	1.0000	.8734
Mode*		.83	.65	.66	.85	1.00	.90
Standard deviation		.14608	.16698	.12772	.17708	.14222	.14519
Variance		.021	.028	.016	.031	.020	.021
Range		.67	.69	.57	.82	.67	.67
Minimum		.33	.20	.34	.18	.33	.33
Maximum		1.00	.89	.91	1.00	1.00	1.00

* Multiple modes exist. The smallest value is shown.

Figure 8.12. Pre- and Post-test Scores for the CAMP Method Group

		Pre-test scores in multiple choice section	Pre-test scores in written section	Total pre-test scores	Post-test scores in written section	Post-test scores in multiple choice section	Total post-test scores
N	Valid	30	30	30	30	30	30
	Missing	0	0	0	0	0	0
Mean		.6339	.7833	.6793	.9412	.9833	.9540
Median		.6727	.8333	.6962	.9455	1.0000	.9620
Mode*		.53	.67	.62	.98	1.00	.99
Standard deviation		.18073	.14615	.13732	.04597	.06710	.04353
Variance		.033	.021	.019	.002	.005	.002
Range		.65	.50	.53	.18	.33	.19
Minimum		.24	.50	.38	.82	.67	.81
Maximum		.89	1.00	.91	1.00	1.00	1.00

* Multiple modes exist. The smallest value is shown.

Figure 8.13. Pre- and Post-test Scores for the Limited Training Group

		Pre-test scores in multiple choice section	Pre-test scores in written section	Total pre-test scores	Post-test scores in written section	Post-test scores in multiple choice section	Total post-test scores
N	Valid	30	30	30	30	30	30
	Missing	0	0	0	0	0	0
Mean		.6061	.8167	.6700	.8448	.8778	.8549
Median		.6273	.8333	.6772	.8636	.8333	.8797
Mode*		.65	.83	.66	.85	.83	.90
Standard deviation		.16074	.15381	.12433	.11175	.09722	.09090
Variance		.026	.024	.015	.012	.009	.008
Range		.64	.67	.49	.51	.33	.41
Minimum		.20	.33	.34	.49	.67	.59
Maximum		.84	1.00	.84	1.00	1.00	1.00

* Multiple modes exist. The smallest value is shown.

Figure 8.14. Pre- and Post-test Scores for the Control Group

		Pre-test scores in multiple choice section	Pre-test scores in written section	Total pre-test scores	Post-test scores in written section	Post-test scores in multiple choice section	Total post-test scores
N	Valid	30	30	30	30	30	30
	Missing	0	0	0	0	0	0
Mean		.5994	.8278	.6688	.6327	.8278	.6920
Median		.6455	.8333	.6899	.6727	.8333	.6962
Mode*		.65	.83	.63	.67	.83	.62
Standard deviation		.16523	.14171	.12741	.17566	.18817	.13788
Variance		.027	.020	.016	.031	.035	.019
Range		.64	.50	.49	.67	.67	.57
Minimum		.24	.50	.42	.18	.33	.33
Maximum		.87	1.00	.91	.85	1.00	.90

* Multiple modes exist. The smallest value is shown.

the fact that there was no contamination of the controls by the study group members. After the intervention, the control group's mean score changed from 67 to 69 percent, an increase of 2 percentage points. In addition, the variance increased for two of the three test measures. Variances for the pre-test were .03, .02, and .02. Post-test variances were .03, .04, and .02.

Two tables, figures 8.15 and 8.16, summarize pre- and post-test scores for all study participants. The first shows pre- and post-test scores for the multiple choice, the written section, and the overall test, broken out by group. The second shows the variances of these scores. The variances demonstrate findings consistent with the study hypotheses. First, the variances show some improvement for any group receiving training intervention. Second, the variances show that the CAMP Method group had higher postintervention positive variances than either of the other two groups. The CAMP Method group variance was +27 percent and the limited training group variance was +19 percent. Finally, the control group showed literally no variance (or improvement) in test scores. The control group variance was +2 percent.

CHAPTER SUMMARY

The CAMP Method training program uses both measurement and audiovisual training tools. The measurement tools are the attitudes and opinions survey, self-efficacy questionnaires, and the clinical documentation test. These measurements serve three purposes. First, the test results allow you to identify areas in need of attention for each individual physician. Second, instructors should use the results to focus initial and follow-up training. Third, the test results are a record of training and what the physician learned. The tools include an agenda and schedule of training activities, PowerPoint studies, case studies, a short movie, and a session evaluation.

STEPS YOU CAN TAKE TODAY

- View the movie contained on the resource disc with your colleagues. Discuss how you could incorporate the movie into a training session.

Figure 8.15. Pre- and Post-test Scores by Group

Clinical Documentation Test	All Groups	Control Group	CAMP Method Group	Limited Training Group
Multiple choice—pre-test	81%	82%	78%	82%
Multiple choice—post-test	90%	83%	98%	89%
Written—pre-test	61%	60%	63%	61%
Written—post-test	81%	63%	94%	84%
Total score—pre-test	67%	67%	68%	67%
Total score—post-test	84%	69%	95%	86%

Figure 8.16. Pre- and Post-test Score Variances by Group

Clinical Documentation Test	All Groups	Control Group	CAMP Method Group	Limited Training Group
Multiple choice	+.09	+.01	+.20	+.07
Written	+.20	+.03	+.31	+.23
Total score	+.16	+.02	+.27	+.19

- Review the PowerPoint slides. If you have a current program, determine if there are any slides that you could add to your current clinical documentation training sessions.
- Review the case studies. If you have a current program, determine if there are any studies that you could add to your current clinical documentation training sessions.

9. Levels of Physician Training: Who Gets What Training?

T HIS CHAPTER takes the basic training described in chapter 7 to the next level by addressing who gets what clinical documentation training. The primary focus of this book is to establish, develop, and maintain a solid training program in clinical documentation. Within the first two years of implementing the program, all active physicians should be expected to have successfully completed the basic training program. Then, each year, new physicians and residents enroll in the program and complete it. In addition, follow-up clinical documentation training should be provided for the physicians. The amount and type of training will depend on the issues identified through the program as well as by the organization's ultimate vision for clinical documentation.

Case studies about physician specialty training are presented in this chapter, along with recommendations for designing specific programs for medical and surgical specialists, hospitalists, physician leaders, residents, fellows, and house staff. Specific recommendations on how to operationalize and sustain an educational program and incentivize physicians to participate in the training are included, as are recommendations for follow-up training.

We will begin by addressing the training of all physicians. A higher priority for clinical documentation training will be assigned to certain groups of physicians. These groups are identified in the chapter. Within each group of physicians, continuing education considerations will also be discussed.

INITIAL CLINICAL DOCUMENTATION IMPLEMENTATION PLAN

A sample plan for rolling out clinical documentation training using one internal team is provided below. Although a plan might take two years (24 months), all initial training, including make-up sessions, should ideally be completed within the first 18 months of the training program. Smaller and less complex organizations will take less time to implement the initial training. Larger and more complex organizations may take the full 24 months to implement initial training. You will need to tailor your plan to fit the needs of your organization. Some organizations may have the ability to require all active physicians to attend training within the first few months. Most, however, will need to work with longer and more complex time lines.

Of greatest importance is developing a time line and a plan that are realistic and enforceable within your organization. Because clinical documentation is such an essential function, the new program is worth the time it takes to implement correctly. Alternatively, if you need to implement training in a shorter period of time, you will have to hire additional external resources to assist. Even if you do bring in external experts, you should still maintain a core internal training team that includes at least one physician. Internal support increases sustainability.

An optimal plan groups physicians together by specialty. Physicians learn and retain their knowledge better when they are learning with peers. In addition, some details of the case studies could be modified to reflect specialty-specific scenarios. The size of the ideal class (based on the CAMP™ Method study) contains no more than 30 participants. However, if you have the opportunity to provide the training to larger groups of physicians, you can make some modifications. There may be a few points lost in post-test scores as a result, so you will need to determine whether the opportunity is worth the possible loss in the effectiveness of the training. In addition, if you do conduct the training with more than 30 trainees, you will need to lengthen the *asking* component of the program to accommodate the extra number of trainees. For example, if the asking component in session one calls for 10 minutes of discussion time with 30 trainees and your training group

Figure 9.1. Sample Two-year Clinical Documentation Training Plan for Physicians

Physician Group	Month 1	2	3	4	5	6	7	8	9	10	11	12	13	14	15	16	17	18
Hospitalists	▪	▪																
Medicine		▪	▪															
Medicine specialties		▪	▪															
General surgeons			▪	▪														
Surgery specialties				▪														
OB/GYN Newborn					▪													
ED physicians					▪	▪	▪											
Radiologists								▪	▪									
Anesthesiologists				▪	▪													
Residents	▪	▪	▪	▪														
Fellows				▪	▪													
Employed primary care physicians						▪	▪	▪	▪									
Employed specialists and surgeons			▪	▪	▪													
Session one make up for medicine specialties											▪	▪						
Session two make up for medicine specialties														▪	▪			
Session one make up for surgical specialties													▪	▪				
Session two make up for surgical specialties																	▪	▪

size is 60, then you should double the amount of time to 20 minutes to allow most of the members an opportunity to speak.

The amount of time needed to implement the training for your physicians may be more or less than the time line above, based on the number of physicians in each specialty and your organization's ability, if necessary, to conduct sessions concurrently. For example, most organizations identify a two-month period for training per specialty with overlaps for most. The two-month period includes two weeks for the pre- and post-testing. So, for most specialties and physician groups, if there are 30 people or less and they can be trained concurrently, it will take one additional week for the pre- and post-testing. The schedule shown in figure 9.1 reflects consideration for both unexpected issues and instructor availability. You will need to determine the timing that works best for your organization, given your resources.

ADDRESSING SPECIFIC TRAINING NEEDS

The size, complexity, and breadth of the clinical documentation program will determine specific initial training needs. For example, the program breadth for a six-hospital system with 72 clinics and an academic medical center will most likely be greater than for a two-hospital nonteaching system. The number of physicians to be trained initially, as well as on an ongoing basis, should also be taken into account. For example, if you plan to perform all training with in-house physician instructors and clinical documentation experts, your resources may only be able to accommodate training for 100 physicians per month. If you have 2,000 physicians on your attending staff, the initial implementation will take at least two years. You will need to consider resources, budget, and timeline, based on the organization's vision for clinical documentation, to determine whether or not to bring in outside experts to assist with training.

PHYSICIAN CLINICAL DOCUMENTATION LEADERS—TRAIN THE TRAINER

If your organization does not already have a physician on staff who is a high quality documenter (based on test scores) and is a trained or certified clinical documentation instructor, you will probably need to arrange to have an outside expert provide training. If you do already have a physician candidate, but the individual needs training, you can arrange to have the physician trained via a train-the-trainer program.

If you do chose to bring in outside expertise to provide initial clinical documentation training to your physicians, you will want to ensure that you have at least one physician leader who receives intensive training while the experts are on site. It is also important to have at least one physician on your staff who is trained in clinical documentation instruction for compliance purposes. By properly training physician leaders of the staff to deliver training, you send the message that clinical documentation is the responsibility of the physician. Although the hospital or healthcare system may provide support, ask questions, and track quality, it is ultimately up to each individual physician to document with high quality and answer questions that might arise about her documentation. No two cases are the same, and the physician's knowledge of the patient, combined with her clinical expertise and training in high quality clinical documentation practices, will ensure the best possible clinical documentation for the patient and the healthcare organization.

ACADEMIC MEDICAL CENTERS AND TEACHING HOSPITALS

Academic medical centers have more opportunities to support and improve clinical documentation than nonteaching hospitals. However, unless the organization trains tightly and consistently, those additional opportunities could result in a multiplication of documentation problems. For example, in the average teaching hospital, six different physicians document in a patient's record. Unless the physicians are all consistently trained to document using the same criteria for high quality clinical documentation, the patient's record could contain conflicting documentation. These conflicts require more intervention to clear up and can result in significant resource usage by the organization. The conflicts, unless they are completely resolved, can also result in compliance risks for the organization. The following recommendations provide guidance on how to ensure tight, consistent clinical documentation training for house staff and other physicians in the teaching hospital setting.

Chief residents. Identify at least one chief resident to lead the clinical documentation training program. The chief resident should participate in the clinical documentation intensive training sessions provided by experts at your facility. He should then be able to provide clinical documentation training and support to other residents.

Residents—year one. First-year residents can play a key, ongoing role in your clinical documentation program. In order for a continuous intensive first-year residency clinical documentation training program to work, the organization needs support from the residency director, attending physicians (in supporting roles), and chief resident. Additionally, the program must be mandatory for all first-year residents.

Many organizations use first-year residents as the backbone of their clinical documentation training program. In fact, in several hospitals in New York City, first-year residents from all specialties participated in the initial training described in this book. In one facility, first-year residents attended monthly documentation training sessions for the entire first year of their residencies. The attending physicians supported them and were called in for mediation when there was conflicting documentation. The sessions were good learning experiences for both the attending physicians and the residents. Not only did the organization see an improvement in the reliability of its coded data during the first year of the clinical documentation training program, the improvement maintained itself for the next three years as the residents progressed through their entire residency program at the hospital. Because the hospitals continued the training with each first-year residency class, the impact continued in sustainability and value to the organization. In order for a continuous intensive first-year residency clinical documentation program to work, the organization needs support from the residency director, attending physicians (in supporting roles), and chief resident involvement. And, the program must be mandatory for all first-year residents.

Residents—year two through four. If first year residents have completed initial clinical documentation training, then second-, third-, and fourth-year residents should be involved in at least a quarterly follow-up training process. This training process should be based upon identified issues in residents' documentation in patient records.

Staff attending physicians. Staff attending physicians should serve in a support role to residents, particularly when a documentation conflict needs to be resolved. In order for the attending physicians to provide adequate support, they must also be involved in some level of ongoing clinical documentation training. If not, the organization may find itself in a situation similar to one teaching hospital in the Northeast. At that hospital, residents were trained rigorously on clinical documentation. However, most attending physicians chose not to attend the training sessions held for them. In fact, many attending physicians stated that it was the resident's responsibility to provide documentation in the record. This hospital treated a fairly large HIV population. And the residents were trained in the documentation rules at the time (circa 2000–2005) that required the physician to use the specific term AIDS or AIDS-related condition when the patient in fact had AIDS, and was not just HIV positive. The residents began documenting AIDS whenever the patient's clinical condition supported the diagnosis. However, the attending physicians, most of whom were unaware of the documentation rule change, continued to document HIV in their final progress notes. When the hospital coder received the record, she was unable to code it without requesting conflict resolution from the attending physician. The process took almost nine months to resolve, costing the organization valuable time and money. It required intensive one-on-one training of the attending physicians who treated HIV patients to ensure they were documenting consistently with the criteria for high quality clinical documentation. The intensive one-on-ones required involvement from the CEO of the system as well as from several senior managers and the consulting team. The entire problem could have been averted if the executive team had been clear with the attending physicians that the clinical documentation training was required, not optional.

THE ROLE OF HOSPITALISTS IN CLINICAL DOCUMENTATION PROGRAMS

Hospitalists can serve as the frontline clinical documentation team for the hospital. Because of their role in seeing most, if not all, patients, hospitalists should be trained extensively in clinical documentation. In fact, one of the hospitals in New York City that rolled out an intensive first-year residency training program also implemented an intensive hospitalist training program. The program was anchored using the CAMP Method training. Following successful completion of the two two-hour sessions, the hospitalists were assigned a clinical documentation mentor, an outside physician expert who provided on-unit review and feedback of their documentation. At the end of a three-month period of mentoring, the physicians were required to take and pass a rigorous clinical documentation test that included a review of their records and the completion of a testing instrument. As a result of the hospitalists' involvement, this organization benefited from complete documentation and more reliable coding.

FOLLOW-UP TRAINING

Once initial CAMP Method clinical documentation has been provided to all physicians, the program should continue. Follow-up clinical documentation training should be the ongoing responsibility of the clinical documentation department or team in conjunction with the organization's physician instructor. Follow-up training should continue to include the four components of the CAMP Method (coaching, asking, mastering, and peer learning) to ensure high self-efficacy (confidence levels) and competency. You can build these components into follow-up training by referring to the *Compelling Case for Clinical Documentation* manuals and using the activities in the basic training program as models.

Follow-up training should be determined primarily by continuous measures of clinical documentation quality. These measures may be obtained from query rates, documentation audits, physician testing, or feedback from clinicians. Topics can also be driven by regulatory changes. If documentation requirements change, the clinical documentation training program in your organization can be the vehicle for informing physicians about the change. Furthermore, if you use either your own internal learning system or the CAMP Method Web site subscription service, you can test all physicians' knowledge to identify deficiencies and use the results to support compliance in this area.

CHAPTER SUMMARY

Deciding which physicians in your organization receive clinical documentation training and planning when they will receive it is an important function. Depending on the size of your organization, implementation of training may vary; but generally, you should plan on 12 to 18 months for complete implementation of the training. Implementing clinical documentation training using the CAMP Method requires the commitment and dedication of both your physicians and your organization. The process is resource intensive, but the impact is worth the investment.

Employed physicians can play a key role in clinical documentation program training. For teaching hospitals, residents can play an important ongoing support role. For organizations that employ hospitalists, this group too can play a key role. If yours is a large organization, hospitalists can be trained first through a train-the-trainer program. Hospitalists can then assist with the training program rollout. Their involvement may have a positive impact on physician motivation and sustainability of the program.

STEPS YOU CAN TAKE

- Review the sample implementation plan. What differences would you envision this plan would need for your organization?
- Discuss with your colleagues a train-the-trainer approach for training physicians in your organization to take a leadership role. Can you identify six physicians in your organization who might be candidates for such a role?
- If yours is a teaching facility, can you imagine an essential role for residents in the clinical documentation program? Who would you speak with to propose a pilot-training session?

10. Teaching and the Theory of High Quality Clinical Documentation

THE THEORY of high quality clinical documentation (HQCD) is derived from evidence-based medicine as well as the regulatory and legal requirements discussed in prior chapters. The theory states that *if* the seven criteria of high quality clinical documentation are consistently applied to clinical documentation, *then* clinical documentation quality will be high and the accuracy of care, quality indicators, reimbursement, healthcare planning, and research (the activities that clinical documentation impacts) will be improved.

Evidence-based medicine entails practicing medicine using only the best scientific data available. Volumes 1 and 2 of this book present all of the scientific data available from peer reviewed journals that illustrate and attest to the current problems with quality of clinical documentation and the potential for a self-efficacy based intervention to improve quality. In *Evidence-Based to Value-Based Medicine*, the authors argue that evidence-based medical (EBM) data enable clinicians to deliver higher quality care.[1] The authors further state that learning about EBM improves the efficacy, or confidence, with which physicians gather and process new information. However, confidence will only increase if physicians can trust the EBM data. And data can only be trusted if it is derived from high quality clinical documentation. Figure 10.1 demonstrates the relationship between the criteria for high quality clinical documentation (HQCD) and the activities that it impacts.

In *The Gold Standard: The Challenge of Evidence-Based Medicine and*

Figure 10.1. The Relationship Between High Quality Clinical Documentation (HQCD) and the Activities it Impacts

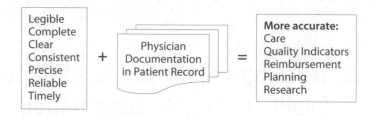

Standardization of Health Care, Timmermans and Berg use the evolution of patient medical records as an analogy for evidence-based medicine. EBM is about creating a standard in medical care. There are four kinds of standards used in EBM: design, terminology, performance, and procedural.[2] The authors point out that the notion of patient-centered medical record keeping, begun in the U.S. at the turn of the twentieth century, like evidence-based medicine, also encompasses all four types of standardization. Additionally, Timmermans and Berg describe the evolution of patient record-keeping standards from the 1920s, when the American College of Surgeons was the only regulating body for medical record content, to the rigorous requirements of Medicare, the Joint Commission, and the state departments of health.

Just like evidence-based medicine, patient medical records need to continue to evolve and improve. The focus on high quality clinical documentation is a good example of this evolution. Furthermore, the CAMP™ Method training program presented in this book is based upon an information-gathering and evaluation process similar to that used in evidence-based medicine. This characteristic makes the training akin to evidence-based medicine. Sharing the basis of the training with physician trainees may create a greater likelihood for them to understand the importance of attaining and maintaining high quality clinical documentation.

BUILDING BLOCKS: CRITERIA FOR HIGH QUALITY CLINICAL DOCUMENTATION

The building blocks of clinical documentation quality include the following seven criteria: legible, complete, clear, consistent, precise, reliable, and timely. The first six are focused on a review process because they can be corrected after the fact, if necessary. While it is preferred that all clinical documentation entered into the patient's medical record be consistent with high quality criteria during the initial entry, even laws and healthcare regulations recognize the need to make corrections or clarifications after the fact. HIPAA gives the patient the right to ask the healthcare provider to correct inaccurate documentation or rewrite illegible information in the record at any time after the initial entry is made. The last of the criteria, timeliness, is one criterion that cannot be corrected after the fact since once an entry is late, it remains late. Listed below are the seven criteria for high quality clinical documentation. These descriptions include an initial definition taken from the *Oxford English Dictionary*,[3] a description of how the criterion can be applied to patient medical record documentation, and examples of documentation that meet, or fail to meet, the criterion (with the exception of legibility and timeliness).

Note for readers and instructors with a coding background: In most of the cases when documentation does not meet the criteria for high quality, it will most certainly impact the accuracy of the coding assignment. While it is important for health information managers and the hospital management to know this, physicians may not appreciate being reminded over and over again about the relationship between their documentation deficiencies and coding. Therefore, it is recommended that you address the relationship between documentation and coding in the general principles section of the training. Offering frequent reminders about the impact on coding can have a negative impact on the physician's willingness to listen and cooperate. Staying focused on the overall vision of the hospital—while explaining the criteria for high quality clinical documentation, as was done in the CAMP Method clinical documentation training—is more likely to elicit a positive response from the physicians.

Legible. *Clear enough to be read and easily deciphered.* The legibility of physician documentation is often joked about, but it is actually a very serious issue. Legibility is addressed as a requirement for clinical documentation by every regulatory body and law that addresses medical record content. The most recent nod to the importance of legibility came when HIPAA gave patients the right to ask for clarification of illegible information in their records. The inability to read a record entry is usually due to the fact that the physician's handwriting is indecipherable. Illegible handwriting is usually the result of a rushed or careless documentation practice. As we evolve towards the electronic medical record (EMR), handwriting becomes less of an issue. However, other inherent risks occur in the rushed or careless use of an EMR, which are discussed in later chapters.

Complete. *Having the maximum content. Thorough.* In clinical documentation, this criterion means that the physician has thoroughly addressed all concerns in the patient record. Concerns apply to anything from the patient's initial complaint (did the physician provide a working and final diagnosis?) to the ordering of tests (did the physician document the reason for the tests?) to abnormal diagnostic test results (did the physician document the clinical significance of any abnormal diagnostic test?).

Documentation that does not meet criteria for completeness:

Physician orders comprehensive blood chemistries. The tests show low sodium levels, low magnesium levels, and low potassium levels. The physician does not document diagnoses to represent any of these abnormal results, nor does he document that the results are clinically insignificant.

Documentation that meets criteria for completeness:

In the example above, the physician documents the following in the patient's progress notes on the day after the test results were received:

Na 131 Mg 1.3 K+ 3.1; Patient dehydrated with hypomagnesemia. Potassium within normal limits for this patient given CAD and hypertensive medication. The physician should not document a diagnosis if the clinical evidence did not support it. However, if the abnormal test results do not support a diagnosis, then the physician should document, *abnormal test results are clinically insignificant.*

Clear. *Unambiguous. Intelligible. Not vague.* Vagueness and ambiguity have always been major deficiencies in clinical documentation and, in this case, apply to documentation that does not totally describe what is wrong with the patient. For example, if a patient presents with a symptom such as chest pain and the physician provides no other insight in his documentation, it would be considered vague. If there is no clinical evidence for any diagnosis, then the appropriate documentation would be, *"chest pain etiology undetermined."*

Documentation that does not meet criteria for clarity:
Patient presents with syncope. The physician orders a CT scan and MRI of the brain, EKG, and blood tests, all of which are within normal limits. The physician's final diagnosis on discharge is *syncope.*

Documentation that meets criteria for clarity:
In the above example, the following documentation would meet criteria for clarity, assuming that the appropriate clinical indicators were present:
Syncope, etiology undetermined
Syncope, possible bradycardia
Syncope, probable transient ischemic attack (TIA)

Consistent. *Not contradictory.* Clinical documentation about a patient that contradicts itself from one progress note to the next, or among documentation from different physicians, is deficient. The overall rule is that when another physician's documentation conflicts with the attending physician's documentation, and the attending is unavailable to state otherwise, the attending physician's documentation takes precedence. However, if the attending physician has provided documentation that appears to contradict itself, he must clarify and add an addendum to the discharge summary or a final progress note. It is always best to ask for clarification whenever there is inconsistent documentation in a patient record.

Documentation that does not meet criteria for consistency:

Patient is admitted by her primary care physician with vertigo and confusion. The primary care physician documents the patient's preliminary diagnosis as *TIA* and asks for a neurology consult. The neurologist examines the patient and documents the diagnosis in his final consultation as cerebrovascular accident (*CVA*). The attending physician provides no further documentation regarding the patient's diagnosis. (In this case, the attending physician and the neurologist's diagnoses are inconsistent.)

Documentation that meets criteria for consistency:

The attending physician is asked to rereview the neurologist's consultation. The attending physician adds a final progress note to the patient's record that states the final diagnosis is *CVA*.

Precise. *Accurate. Exact. Strictly defined.* Detail, if available and clinically appropriate, is an important component of every patient's medical record. The more detailed the physician's documentation, the more representative and accurate the clinical documentation in the patient's record is likely to be.

Documentation that does not meet criteria for precision:

Patient is admitted with chest pain, shortness of breath, fever, and cough. Chest X-ray shows aspiration pneumonia. The physician's final documented diagnosis for the patient is *pneumonia*.

Documentation that meets criteria for precision:

The physician reviews the chest X-ray and documents the patient's final diagnosis in the discharge summary as *aspiration pneumonia*.

Reliable. *Trustworthy. Safe. Yielding the same result when repeated.* This criterion relates to treatment provided to the patient and whether the physician's documentation supports the treatment. For example, a physician orders a blood transfusion for a patient who has an upper gastrointestinal bleed and severely low hemoglobin and hematocrit

Figure 10.2. Criteria for High Quality Clinical Documentation

Documentation criteria	Example/description
Legibility	Required under all government and regulatory agencies
Completeness	All abnormal test results have documentation regarding clinical significance of the test result (JCAHO requirement)
Clarity	Unambiguous documentation, especially in the case of a symptom principal diagnosis: instead of chest pain use GERD (if supported); instead of syncope use dehydration (if supported)
Consistency	Agreement between two or more treating physicians, or resolution of any conflicting documentation upon discharge
Precision/Detail	Specific diagnosis documented, when it is supported (anemia vs acute or chronic blood loss anemia)
Reliability	Treatment provided only with documentation of the condition being treated (Lasix, CHF documented; KCL administered, hypokalemia documented)

levels. The physician's diagnosis for the patient is a bleeding gastric ulcer. The physician's diagnosis of a bleeding gastric ulcer does not appear to be completely reliable based on the treatment given. Blood transfusion is usually given to treat anemia. If the physician documents bleeding gastric ulcer with acute blood loss anemia (if clinically indicated), based on the treatment given, this is a reliable diagnosis.

Documentation that does not meet reliability:
Patient is admitted with shortness of breath and chest pain. The patient is treated with Lasix, oxygen, and Theophylline. The physician's final documented diagnosis for the patient is *acute exacerbation of chronic obstructive pulmonary disease (COPD)*.

Documentation that does meet reliability:
The patient was given Lasix to treat an acute and chronic heart failure (CHF). The physician amends the final progress note to reflect the final diagnosis: *Acute exacerbation of chronic bronchitis and COPD; acute CHF*. In this case, the patient had bronchitis with the COPD, so the initial documentation did not meet criteria for both reliability and precision.

Timely. *At the right time.* Timeliness of clinical documentation is essential to the best treatment of the patient. The EMR can help with timeliness, but until an EMR is implemented in every hospital, physicians need to be as timely as possible with documentation. In addition to daily progress note entries and timely discharge summaries, physicians also need to be timely with diagnoses that are present on admission. Hospitals need to report when a diagnosis was present on admission as evidence that the condition did not develop in the hospital. Present on admission documentation impacts research, reimbursement, and planning.

Figure 10.2 is a summary of criteria for high quality clinical documentation along with representative examples. This can also be used in the slide presentation during the training session with physicians.

THE RELATIONSHIP BETWEEN CLINICAL DOCUMENTATION AND CODING

Because patient information is used for many purposes beyond current treatment, it is important for physicians to understand the basic relationship between their clinical documentation and how it is translated into coded data. The instructor should explain this in the beginning of the program, as denoted by the ordering of the PowerPoint slides. However, as noted above, the concept should be repeated with care to avoid overuse and a potentially negative reaction from the physicians. The slide shown in figure 10.3 demonstrates this relationship and can be used to explain this concept during training.

The next slide (figure 10.4) can be used to provide some additional detail about documentation and coding. This information can be useful to physicians in their own office practices as well.

Finally, if the organization has, or will have, a clinical documentation program in place with concurrent querying, it is important to explain this process to the physicians as well.

The slides shown in figures 10.5–10.8 can be used to explain this process.

Figure 10.3. Relationship Between Clinical Documentation and Coding

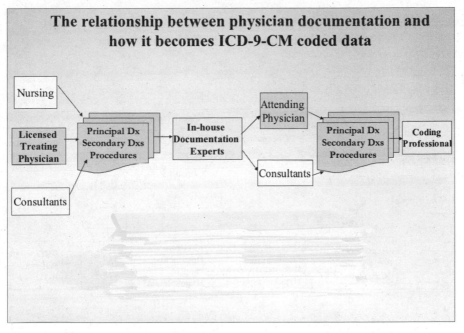

Figure 10.4. Documentation and Coding

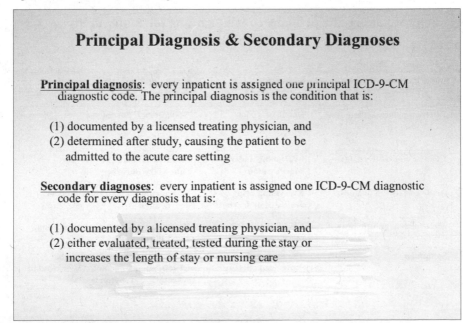

Principal Diagnosis & Secondary Diagnoses

Principal diagnosis: every inpatient is assigned one principal ICD-9-CM diagnostic code. The principal diagnosis is the condition that is:

(1) documented by a licensed treating physician, and
(2) determined after study, causing the patient to be
   admitted to the acute care setting

Secondary diagnoses: every inpatient is assigned one ICD-9-CM diagnostic code for every diagnosis that is:

(1) documented by a licensed treating physician, and
(2) either evaluated, treated, tested during the stay or
   increases the length of stay or nursing care

Figure 10.5. Opportunities to Improve Documentation

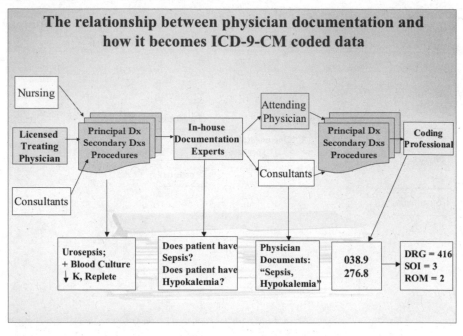

Figure 10.6. HQCD Considerations 1

What are the primary considerations for high quality clinical data?

Important considerations	Document . . .	Examples: if present or *suspected* document . . .
Patient's principal diagnosis	Detail, precision	*"Aspiration"* pneumonia; *"Acute"* renal failure; cerebral *"infarct"*
Chronic co-existing diagnoses	Everything under consideration	COPD; CHF; seizure disorder; pulmonary fibrosis
Acute co-existing diagnoses	Everything being evaluated or treated	Malnutrition; respiratory failure; dehydration
Abnormal diagnostic tests	The clinical significance of	Hyponatremia; mitral regurgitation; atrial fibrillation
Symptoms	The etiology or "suspected etiology"	Instead of chest pain . . . possible GERD; angina due to CAD; instead of syncope . . . arrhythmia

Figure 10.7. HQCD Considerations 2

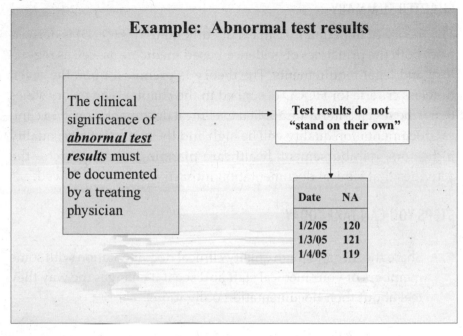

Figure 10.8. HQCD Considerations 3

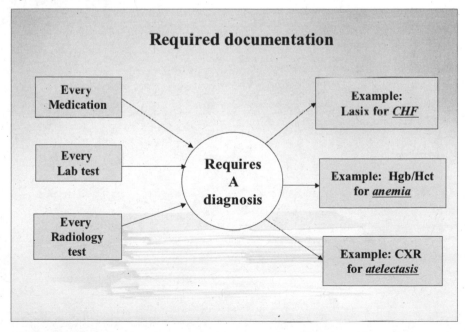

CHAPTER SUMMARY

The theory of high quality clinical documentation (HQCD) is derived from both the principles of evidence-based medicine as well as regulatory and legal requirements. The theory is premised upon the seven timeless criteria for HQCD described in the chapter. The theory states that *if* the seven criteria are applied to clinical documentation, *then* clinical documentation quality will be high and the quality of care, quality indicators, reimbursement, healthcare planning, and research—the activities that clinical documentation impacts—will be improved.

STEPS YOU CAN TAKE TODAY

- Share the theory of high quality clinical documentation with some members of your medical staff and see if it changes the way they feel about their documentation obligations.

11. Using Outcomes Measures to Design Follow-up Training

THERE ARE TWO PRIMARY METHODS for measuring the outcomes of clinical documentation training: audits of documentation practices and retesting of physicians on documentation concepts and principles. Both have pros and cons. The first method, audits of documentation, is more reliable, but requires a sizeable amount of staff time to perform. The second, retesting, is less reliable than audits, and requires time from the physician to complete. Either methodology, or both methodologies, can be worked into your program. Follow-up training has the greatest impact if it is designed to target identified weaknesses in the system. Specifically, these are weaknesses or deficiencies of individual physicians or groups of physicians. Focusing on specific issues is an efficient use of everyone's time.

This chapter describes implementation suggestions that you can use to obtain support for additional resources needed. Among them is tying your measurement efforts back to the values, vision, and mission statement (VVMS) for your organization's clinical documentation program. Your clinical documentation quality (CDQ) VVMS, in turn, should directly tie into your organization's overall vision and mission. By making these connections, you are more likely to obtain support for additional resources. In addition, you are more likely to be successful with your efforts by showing a positive impact, an impact that is measured by your organization's VVMS.

This chapter also describes the primary measurement processes of documentation audits and testing. A secondary method for measurement

Figure 11.1. Hospital ABC: Top Principal Diagnosis Changes in Response to a Query

Changed to this principal diagnosis . . .	# Times
Sepsis (from bacteremia)	3
Acute congestive heart failure (from CHF NOS)	3
Respiratory failure (from other respiratory diagnoses)	2

involves using operational measures used in the day-to-day clinical documentation program. These may be measures like query rates, response rates, and agreement rates, among others. These measures are best used to determine the success of the program operations, not the quality of the documentation. In the interest of saving time and money, some organizations may use these measures to determine both documentation and operational quality. While not recommended, if resource constraints require using this method, you should be aware of the limitations.

THE PRIMARY METHODS FOR MEASURING CLINICAL DOCUMENTATION TRAINING SUCCESS

Clinical Documentation Audits

Every clinical documentation program should have regular audits of the clinical documentation review, query, and response procedures. Because of the contemporaneous nature of the query process, audits are best performed concurrently. Results may be skewed because reviewers know they are being observed. However, the analysis that is generated—from observing a verbal query, for example—can be quite helpful to both the reviewer and the organization. Concurrent review increases expenses and staff time. Therefore, most organizations are more likely to perform clinical documentation audits retrospectively.

A simple way to *audit* clinical documentation activity is to identify, through your clinical documentation software, what the top diagnoses are that are being added in response to a query. Figures 11.1 and 11.2 show the results of an analysis of common principle diagnoses that needed clarification and secondary diagnoses that were often not documented by physicians in a particular academic medical center. This information

Figure 11.2. Hospital ABC: Top Secondary Diagnoses Added in Response to Query

Diagnosis added after query . . .	# Times added on review
Anemia NOS	29
Electrolyte imbalance (hypo- or hypernatremia, hypo- or hyperkalemia, hypo- or hypercalcemia, etc.)	25
Arrhythmias (atrial fibrillation, bradycardia, tachycardia, ventricular tachycardia)	25
Intravenous drug abuse	17
Urinary tract infection	15
Pneumonia	15
Hypertension	15
Reflux esophagitis	12
Obesity	11
Loss of consciousness	11
Chronic renal failure	11
Acute renal failure	11
Tobacco abuse	10
Hypercholesterolemia	10
Dehydration	10
Blood loss anemia	10
CHF	9
Atelectasis	9
Thrombocytopenia	7
Malnourished	7
Hypotension	7
Post-operative infection	6
Diabetes mellitus NOS	6
Coronary atherosclerosis	6

can be used to create training programs specific to the criteria for high quality clinical documentation. To the extent that an organization can use the actual hospital patient records that were queried for clarification, physicians and the hospital will benefit greatly.

Clinical Documentation Post-testing

Your first plan for follow-up clinical documentation testing should be driven by the results of the clinical documentation post-test that the physicians take after they have completed the second clinical documentation training session. Test results can be analyzed by physician, by specialty, or by type of documentation deficiency identified in the testing instrument. The testing instrument is a two-part test with multiple choice questions appearing first and mini-case studies appearing second. You will obtain good information for follow-up education from the mini-case study responses from the physician. By way of example, part 1 and part 2 of the clinical documentation test are provided in figure 11.3. Follow-up testing used to measure training impact will likely contain fewer questions. If physicians take tests manually, you can perform your analysis by reviewing the tests. If physicians take the tests via the CAMP™ Method Web site, a computer analysis will be provided to you with recommendations for the focus of follow-up training.

Clinical Documentation Retesting

Testing can easily be used to continue to drive the content of ongoing clinical documentation training. After the initial clinical documentation training, you will likely need to begin providing training on a service by service basis. The sessions will be focused on the types of issues being seen specifically in cardiology or neurology or orthopedic surgery. Many clinical documentation programs claim to use a specialty-specific training process from the outset. But as a practical matter, the basic criteria for high quality clinical documentation are the same for each specialty and need to be taught as such. What may be different are the examples used. Because we have been able to validate outcomes using the specific tools provided in these manuals for the initial clinical documentation training sessions, we recommend that you use these as well. We cannot guarantee that you won't see a drop-off in post-test scores if you deviate from the training provided during the CAMP Method clinical documentation study. For follow-up training and testing, you can create organization-specific tools and tests; however, it is important to continue to use the CAMP Method techniques for creating the instructional materials.

Figure 11.3. CAMP Method Study Pre- and Post-test for Documentation Quality

---

Part 1: Circle the best answer for each of the multiple choice questions below.

1. Physician documentation in patient records is translated into ICD-9-CM codes. These codes are used to:

   a. rank a hospital's quality of care by organizations such as HealthGrades.com
   b. determine the amount of reimbursement a hospital will receive for patient care
   c. direct healthcare planning and research activities
   d. all of the above

2. A patient's H&P should be documented and available on the patient's record:

   a. at the time of admission
   b. within 24 hours of admission
   c. within 48 hours of admission
   d. by the time of discharge

3. One illegible progress note in a patient's record:

   a. will not have any impact on the patient's care as long as the other notes are legible
   b. will be interpreted based upon the other documentation and test results on the same day
   c. will be treated as though no care was provided on that day
   d. can negatively impact patient care, medical malpractice defense, and reimbursement for the care
   e. both c & d

4. Clinical documentation in an inpatient record can only be translated into an ICD-9-CM code if it is documented by a:

   a. board certified physician
   b. licensed, treating physician
   c. primary care practitioner
   d. consulting physician

Part 2: Document the diagnoses for the patient scenarios described below.

   A. A patient is admitted with abdominal pain and nausea and vomiting. Initial and subsequent lab tests reveal a sodium of 120 and 121. The patient is placed on normal saline 120cc/hr. Document the patient's diagnoses.

   _____

   _____

   _____

   B. You are following a patient post-surgically with a fem-pop bypass. During surgery, the patient lost 300cc of blood. The patient's post-surgical hgb and hct dropped from 13 and 24 to 10 and 21. The patient received 2U of packed red blood cells after surgery. Document any post-operative diagnosis (es) that these lab results and treatment may represent.

   _____

   _____

   _____

C. A patient's urine C&S reveals >100,000 colonies of E. coli and the patient is placed on bactrim. Document any diagnosis that this lab finding and treatment may represent.

_____

_____

_____

D. A patient with pneumonia per chest X-ray has sputum C&S findings of gram negative rods, too numerous to count. Document any diagnosis that this finding may represent.

_____

_____

_____

E. A patient admitted with atrial fibrillation has echocardiogram results of moderate mitral regurgitation and aortic sclerosis. Document any diagnoses these findings may represent.

_____

_____

_____

F. A patient admitted with dehydration has a chest X-ray positive for COPD. Document any diagnoses these findings may represent.

_____

_____

_____

G. A patient is admitted for cardiac catheterization to rule out suspected CAD. The patient has a history of CHF and needs to be placed on Lasix. Document the order for Lasix for this patient.

_____

_____

_____

H. You are following a surgical patient with DM Type II. After surgery the patient's blood glucose reaches 290 and the patient is placed on sliding scale insulin. Document any diagnosis that this finding and treatment may represent.

_____

_____

_____

I. A patient is admitted with chest pain. EGD performed after admission shows GERD. Document any diagnoses that these findings may represent.

_____

_____

_____

J. A patient is admitted with syncope. EKG shows bradycardia. Document any diagnoses that these findings may represent.

_____

_____

_____

K. A patient's EKG is documented with several runs of V-tach. Document any diagnoses that these findings may represent.

_____

_____

_____

CAMP Method study pre-and post-test answer key: total points: 71

Note: words in italics denote the specific concept of clinical documentation being tested in the question.

Part 1: Multiple Choice
[4 points each]

1. d *completeness*
2. b *timeliness*
3. e *legibility*
4. b *clarity*

Part 2: Document the diagnoses for the patient scenarios described below
[5 points each. 4 points each for content. 1 point each for legibility.]

A. Hyponatremia *clarity; legibility*
B. Acute (1 point) blood loss (2 points) anemia (1 point) *precision; completeness; legibility*
C. Urinary tract infection (3 points) due to E. coli (1 point) *precision; completeness; legibility*
D. Gram negative pneumonia *precision; clarity; legibility*
E. Mitral valve regurgitation (2 points) Aortic sclerosis (2 points) *clarity; completeness; legibility*
F. COPD *clarity; completeness; legibility*
G. Lasix for CHF *clarity; legibility*
H. Uncontrolled DM II *precision; completeness; legibility*
I. Chest pain due to GERD *clarity*
J. Syncope due to bradycardia *clarity; legibility*
K. Ventricular tachycardia *clarity; completeness; legibility*

OBTAINING SUPPORT FOR A CLINICAL DOCUMENTATION AUDIT PROGRAM

All components of your clinical documentation program should be audited on at least an annual and preferably on a quarterly basis. The reasons for this are both economic and regulatory in nature. First, you need to prove that the program is a good economic investment for your organization. You may be able to show ongoing operational numbers that support this claim. But to the extent that you can bring in an outside group to validate your internal claims, you will be more likely to receive continued funding, and possibly *additional* funding, in your organization's annual budget. A regular audit will also give you the opportunity to demonstrate how your program furthers the vision and mission of your organization. Clinical documentation quality is an essential component of every healthcare organization's structure. You can show your contributions to continued success of the organization through your work with clinical documentation, the medical staff, and ultimately, the positive impact on patients.

A second reason to conduct, and be able to obtain funding for, external clinical documentation audits is regulatory in nature. There is a relationship between some clinical documentation activities and reimbursement to your organization. As with any such activity, there is a compliance risk. If you have developed your program using the basic principles and criteria of high quality clinical documentation in these manuals, your program has already minimized its compliance risk. But there are other risks that may exist in a clinical documentation program. One of these is the way a query is asked of the physicians. Much has been written about the dangers of a leading query. And while queries should be asked compliantly, if a physician has been trained using the CAMP Method principles we have discussed, he has increased his confidence (self-efficacy) in the process and is well-informed about his responsibility in clinical documentation. Therefore, the possibility that a leading query would sway an educated and well-informed physician is greatly diminished. It is still important to ask queries in a non-leading manner; just keep in mind that your CAMP Method training, if performed correctly, provides an extra layer of protection.

CHAPTER SUMMARY

Audits and testing are the two primary methods for measuring the quality of clinical documentation programs. These measures can also be used to design follow-up training. By implementing a constant audit-training loop for your clinical documentation program, you ensure continuous improvement in quality. Your organization's leadership will likely only continue to fund a program with positive outcome measures. Therefore, ongoing measurement that demonstrates success of the program is likely to help secure its future.

STEPS YOU CAN TAKE TODAY

- Compare your current measures to the suggestions for audits and retesting described in this chapter. Do you believe your current program measures are adequate? If not, how can you use the information in this chapter to improve upon them?
- Ask a few physicians to take the CAMP Method test provided in this chapter. Review their responses. Could you envision your organization using this test instrument in some way to help further the goals of your clinical documentation program?

12. Universal Relevancy: Using the CAMP Method to Train Other Staff

THE BEST PRACTICE for any organization is to require that *all* documentation meets the criteria for high quality clinical documentation regardless of the author. This practice, together with accurate coding practices, ensures that your organization's data is a true reflection of every assessment made of the patient's condition and all the services provided.

While the CAMP™ Method for training was initially developed for physicians, it can be applied universally with minimal modifications. In particular, any organization's clinical documentation function will benefit from training the following individuals or groups: mid-level practitioners—including physician assistants and nurse practitioners—health information professionals, clinical documentation professionals, nurses, and other clinicians such as nutritionists, respiratory therapists, and lab technicians.

RESEARCH SUPPORTS USING THE CAMP METHOD FOR TRAINING CLINICIANS

Self-efficacy, the basis of the CAMP Method, has been used since the 1970s as a foundation for adult learning and the development of training programs. In particular, numerous successful studies have been performed and published in peer reviewed journals involving nurses and other clinicians. Many of these studies show that the use of self-efficacy based training produces positive outcomes. Some of the studies that used self-efficacy based training are listed in figure 12.1. The table shows the researchers, the study type, who was trained, and the focus of the training. All of these studies used the four components of self-efficacy, from which the CAMP Method components are derived.

WHO SHOULD YOU TRAIN?

With the exception of health information management professionals, you can assume that no one in your organization received clinical documentation training in college or professional school. You can further assume that if someone did receive training in clinical documentation from another hospital or healthcare organization, the training varied in quality and quantity from place to place. Because of the lack of standardization in training in the principles of clinical documentation, every organization needs to determine for itself who, in addition to the physicians, should be trained. The list below identifies most clinicians and others in a healthcare organization who should be trained in clinical documentation principles. The list also includes some individuals who may not document in records and may also not be clinicians, but serve in support management roles. Though it is best for managers to have some basic training in clinical documentation, it is essential that, at a minimum, they are familiar with the criteria for high quality clinical documentation.

In the end, you will need to make the final decision about who is included and who is excluded from training in the principles of clinical documentation. But the organization should have the expectation and the vision that everyone who documents in a patient's medical record should do so using only high quality clinical documentation.

Train All Caregivers

Mid-level practitioners. Mid-level practitioners (MLP), which include nurse practitioners and physician assistants, play an important role in delivery of care. In many settings they are considered to be physician extenders. The extent of the MLP's independent activities depends on each state's laws, but in general, most states require physician supervision of the MLP. Because of the important role mid-level practitioners play in patient care, their training in clinical documentation is an essential

Figure 12.1. Summary of Self-Efficacy Studies Involving Clinicians

Researcher(s)	Study Type	Subjects	Focus of the Study
Bravata, 2003	EPP	Residents	Self-directed learning skills
Chung et al., 2004	EPP	Physicians	Bioterrorism
Engel et al., 1997	EPP	Medical students	Diabetic nutrition
Ford-Gilboe & Laschinger, 1997	EPP	Nursing students	Student competency
Gans et al., 1993	EPP	Residents	Cholesterol screening
Goldenberg, Andrusyszn & Iwasiw, 2005	EPP	Nursing students	Student competency
Gramling	SAS	Residents	Cancer screening
Katz, 2005	EPP	Physicians	Counseling obesity
Coffman, Shellman & Bernal, 2004	SAS	Nursing students	Caring for African-American patients
Laschinger & McWilliams, 1999	EPP	Medical students	Counseling: health promotion
Lenzi, 2005	EPP	Residents	Communicating cancer treatment
Mann, 1997	EPP	Medical students	Cholesterol-lowering practices
Mann, 2005	EPP	Medical students	Cholesterol-lowering practices
Martin, 2005	EPP	Physicians	Communicating/ breast cancer patients
Mavis, 2001	SAS	Medical students	Exam performance
Opacic, 2003	SAS	PA students	Competency
Reich, Bickman & Feflinger, 2004	EPP	Caregivers	Mental health services availability
Sommers, Muller & Chu, 2003	SAS	Medical students	Student competency
Thompson, 1993	SAS	Nursing students	Counseling
Treolar, 2001	SAS	Residents	Emergency medicine
Zapka et al., 1999	SAS	Physicians	Smoking cessation

Key: EPP = educational program with pre- and post-test; SAS = self-assessment survey part of an organization's clinical documentation program.

Nurses. Nurses document more frequently in a patient's medical record than any other caregiver. Much of the nurse's documentation involves recording data such as body temperature, input and output, and other objective and subjective indicators of the patient's current status. A nurse also enters progress notes with other caregivers as integrated progress notes. Nurses review the patient's entire record frequently and are aware of all activity involving the patient. Nurses may be in one of the best positions to identify problems with deficiencies in clinical documentation. However, a nurse's responsibilities need to be focused on giving care to the patient. In addition, because she is documenting in the patient's record, it would be impossible for a nurse to assess her own clinical documentation. Further, many organizations have experimented with different clinical documentation models, and almost all have found that the function of reviewing patient records for quality of clinical documentation produces the best outcomes when performed by individuals whose sole responsibility is to review documentation. Because of their unique position in giving care and providing clinical documentation, all nurses should be trained in the principles of clinical documentation.

Nutritionists. If you do not already know, find out what percentage of patients in your hospital receive nutritional consults. On average, about 20 percent of hospital patients receive consultations from nutritionists and, in general, these are the more complex cases. Nutrition staff members have a unique opportunity to document patient nutritional and metabolic disorders with great precision. However, unless they are trained in the principles, they too are likely to document a patient with malnutrition instead of severe protein calorie malnutrition—or some other more precise diagnosis that represents the patient's condition more clearly. While a nutritionist's documentation cannot be used to translate patient medical record documentation into coded data, it can be used to ask a physician for further clarification if the clinical evidence supports a more precise diagnosis.

Therapists. The list of therapists in every healthcare organization is quite long, and, depending on the patient's condition, different therapists play essential roles in their healing process. You should identify all therapists who care for patients and train them in the principles of clinical documentation. Like nutritionists, each therapist—whether he is involved in respiratory, physical, substance abuse, or another therapy—has an opportunity to document the patient's condition in a precise manner. But unless therapists are trained in the principles of clinical documentation, they are unlikely to produce high quality documentation.

All other caregivers. If you perform an audit of a random sampling of your patient records, you should be able to identify all individuals who document in the clinical component of the patient's record. This can help you prepare a list of everyone in your organization who should be trained in high quality clinical documentation.

Train Noncaregivers Who Document in the Medical Record

Case managers. Case managers are clinician managers with prior caregiving experience. In most organizations, case managers are responsible for coordinating all insurance and other administrative requirements for patients from the time of admission through discharge. They often work in conjunction with discharge planners, but sometimes they are responsible for planning discharge efforts. Case managers are in a unique position to identify potential documentation deficiencies concurrently. Because of the large workload that case managers usually carry, most organizations choose to use the clinical documentation specialist model for concurrent documentation review. However, a partnership between case managers and clinical documentation specialists is essential. If an organization is able to pull together the resources from clinical documentation, nursing, and case management to identify any documentation deficiencies concurrently, and the physician response rate is close to 100 percent, high quality clinical documentation would be ensured.

Discharge planners and social workers. Discharge planners may have a clinical or a social work background. Because they begin the discharge planning process upon the patient's admission, discharge planners and social workers also have the ability to look at concurrent entries in the patient's record and should participate in the training process.

Everyone who documents in the record. Identify the job titles of everyone who documents in your patients' records. This will provide you with a list of all individuals who need training in the principles of clinical documentation. Naturally, you can and should prioritize training needs. Physicians are the most important group for initial training. However, some organizations have implemented clinical documentation training using an *inverse* logic. Essentially, they train all of the clinicians *around* the physician in the hopes that these supporting staff members will be able to carry the responsibility for documentation requirements. Organizations that use the inverse approach usually do so because they have less-than-optimal relationships with their physicians. But taking this approach creates a risk of further harm to hospital–medical staff relations as well as compliance exposure.

Volume 1 addresses methods to align hospital management and physicians behind a clinical documentation initiative. To ensure a successful approach to clinical documentation quality, you must start with the medical staff. You can train other staff concurrently or after the physicians, but physician training should be your top priority. The only exception to this, addressed below, is the clinical documentation specialist. Because these individuals are responsible for training physicians, in conjunction with the physician instructor, they will need to be trained first or be hired into your organization with the appropriate CAMP Method training.

Train Staff Who Evaluate the Content of the Record and their Managers

Training noncaregivers on the principles of clinical documentation helps your organization to (1) promote the vision, (2) provide continuing support for the function, and (3) engender understanding among managers for the complexity of the administrative functions of a clinician.

Clinical documentation staff. In most hospitals, the clinical documentation staff members are primarily responsible for the concurrent review of documentation in the medical record, interacting with physicians and other clinicians to clarify entries that appear to be deficient. By managing the documentation process, these specialists ensure that any corrections, changes, or clarifications that need to be made are consistent with the criteria for high quality clinical documentation. Since they participate in the training process, clinical documentation staff members are generally trained prior to the medical staff. There are entire books written on the clinical documentation function. Our focus here is on the training of the clinical documentation specialists and other individuals. If clinical documentation specialists are not hired by your organization with knowledge of the necessary training and experience, you will need to hire a consulting firm or contract employees to provide that training. During the selection process, you can use the contents of this book to ensure that these contractors have adequate knowledge and experience with clinical documentation principles.

Health information management staff. Credentialed coders are the safety net to ensure that high quality clinical documentation appears in the record and is being used as the basis for the codes they are assigning. Obtaining documentation clarification concurrently, while the patient is still being treated, is the most accurate, reliable, and compliant method to use. However, if necessary and clinically indicated, retrospective inquiries to a physician for the sake of clarification and correction are allowable. Therefore, health information managers and the coding staff should be trained in the principles of high quality clinical documentation. In fact, because part of the training to others involves explanations of how clinical documentation is translated into coded data, health information professionals should be part of the training team.

Nurse managers. Nurse managers should be trained because they play an essential support role to all nursing staff and other clinicians. While they will not be involved in the review or correction of documentation, it is helpful for them to understand the challenges that their staff will encounter when they are asked to consistently produce high quality clinical documentation. This is particularly true since the principles of quality clinical documentation are not yet part of the academic curriculum in nursing schools. Certainly, medical record clinical documentation is an important component of nurse training; but an emphasis on achieving the quality standards described in this book is not yet part of that training. So nurses and nurse managers can only receive that instruction through a program offered by their healthcare organization.

Administrative managers. Nonclinical managers in hospitals should understand the impact that clinical documentation makes on the hospital's quality ratings, reimbursement, planning, and research. However, if managers understand the basics and the requirements of clinicians, it will help them manage the process, support their staff, and continue to ensure budgetary support for the program. The initial testing and training only takes about four hours of the manager's time. Practically speaking, this is a small investment for a return that can have significant impact on the organization.

THE CONTENT OF TRAINING FOR NONPHYSICIANS

Generally, nonphysician clinicians who document in the record should receive the training described in this book. For the other groups mentioned above, the content of the training may need to be modified. In particular, for anyone who is involved in record review and who asks physicians to clarify their documentation, training should be tailored to address this activity. The inquiry process is the key component of a clinical documentation program, and it is managed and created by the individuals responsible for implementing and maintaining the program. Therefore, the procedures for asking physicians to clarify their documentation should be designed to meet your organization's specific needs. For example, your training may address issues such as the best time of the day to approach physicians, whether or not reviewers should be permitted to join grand rounds, and what processes will take place if a physician refuses to respond to an inquiry.

There are a few basic tenets that should drive the content of training for documentation reviewers. These include:

- *Use the criteria for high quality clinical documentation to generate queries.* Your process is standard and compliant as long as inquiries are only (and always) asked when one or more of the criteria for high quality clinical documentation has not been met.
- *Ask questions in a non-leading manner.* In an organization where physicians are appropriately trained and responsible for their documentation, *how* a question is asked is not a significant issue.

However, because most physicians today are not yet adequately trained and responsible, the manner of questioning must be done in such a way that physicians understand they are not being told to document in any specific way. They are just being notified that their documentation is deficient by not meeting one or more of the criteria for high quality clinical documentation. Physicians should correct their documentation using their own professional, clinical judgment, relying on their clinical documentation training. This aspect of the questioning process should be taught during the training to coders and clinical documentation specialists.

- *Record every question that is asked.* For compliance and operational purposes, it is important to record every query that is asked. This concept should be discussed during the training of any individual who will ask a physician to clarify his documentation.

PEER LEARNING FOR NONPHYSICIANS (OR WHO SHOULD DO THE TRAINING?)

In the section about training for physicians, we discussed in detail the fact that the CAMP Method requires trainees to be instructed by someone whom they respect as knowledgeable; but, at the same time, the trainer must have professional experience similar to the trainees. The best way to address this issue is to team up a member of the clinical group to be trained with the physician and clinical documentation specialist instructor team. An example of how this was done at one teaching hospital is described in the case study below.

CASE STUDY: ANCILLARY CLINICIANS CAN PLAY A KEY ROLE IN CLINICAL DOCUMENTATION

The nutritionists at a 350-bed teaching hospital in the Southwest were very interested in participating in the clinical documentation program that was just being launched at the hospital. Maryanne, the director of the nutrition department, had previously worked at a regional academic medical center that had implemented a clinical documentation program with which she was involved. The medical center was sure that Maryanne's staff could make an impact on the physicians.

They decided to have Maryanne's staff trained in the basics of clinical documentation and for them to communicate, when necessary, with the clinical documentation specialists.

The first step of the program would generally involve formal training sessions with the entire staff in the nutrition department. In this case, however, the hospital decided that it made sense to train Maryanne first since she was such a strong proponent of the process. By training Maryanne, it would allow her to obtain more knowledge about the program and the responsibilities of her team. It would also allow her to make a better determination about the level of involvement she was willing to commit her staff to regarding the program. Finally, by having Maryanne learn the process first, she could become part of the instructional team that trained her staff. From a CAMP Method perspective, this is the best approach to take for optimal and sustainable learning.

Maryanne was trained by the hospital's physician leader and the clinical documentation manager. She even spent time on the units reviewing records in addition to her classroom training. As she was learning, Maryanne spoke about the experience to her staff in a positive way, and she was excited to have them trained as well. When it came time to do the staff training, the physician–clinical documentation manager team led most of the training, but there were several components that Maryanne was asked to present. In addition, she commented often to the group about her experiences reviewing documentation on the units. Because of the nutrition staff's expertise, the case examples that involved nutrition or metabolic disorders were focused on during the training. The entire nutrition department was very excited about getting started. By the end of their training session, they decided, along with the clinical documentation team, that the nutritionists would have a specific role in documenting clearly in their progress notes or reports whenever a patient met the clinical criteria for malnutrition, obesity, morbid obesity, and similar disorders. The clinical documentation specialists would then be able to generate queries. The nutritionists even designed their own pocket card to refer to and give out to physicians. A copy of the contents of this card appears in figure 12.2.

This team effort was successful for the organization and produced improved documentation almost immediately in nutritional and

Figure 12.2. Clinical Documentation Pocket Guide Designed by Nutrition Staff

---

Clinical Documentation Guidelines
Nutrition and Metabolism

Detailed documentation using the following terminology will accurately reflect the severity of illness under treatment.

✓ Use of TPN or Tube Feeds—Be sure to include the precise diagnosis supporting the use of TPN or Tube Feeds

· Examples of Diagnoses supporting the use of TPN

➢ Severe malnutrition
➢ Protein–calorie malnutrition
➢ Moderate malnutrition

Remember to always qualify malnutrition with a descriptor: mild, moderate, or severe, protein–calorie

Document specific metabolic disorders when appropriate. Such as:

✓ Cachexia	✓ Acidosis
✓ Bulimia	✓ Alkalosis
✓ Persistent vegetative state	✓ Morbid obesity
✓ Anorexia	✓ Fluid overload

Avoid the use of medical shorthand and document the following metabolic conditions using the appropriate terminology.

✓ Hypernatremia	✓ Hypokalemia
✓ Hyponatremia	✓ Vitamin A deficiency
✓ Hypercalcemia	✓ Vitamin B deficiency
✓ Hypocalcemia	✓ B12 deficiency
✓ Hyperkalemia	

---

metabolic disorders. The process was sustained because the group used the CAMP Method for training, which encouraged a strong sense of self-efficacy. It was important that the director of the department was groomed to participate in the peer learning aspect of the training process. It was also important that the nutrition staff members were able to express their concerns about the role they were going to play and that they had input into what their role would look like. This correlated with the asking and coaching aspects of the CAMP methodology.

COACHING FOR NONPHYSICIANS

Coaching encourages trainees, assuring them that they can do the job being asked of them. Trainees will only respond to coaching from credible trainers whom they respect. In addition, coaching is most effective when the individual doing the coaching has successfully performed the activity they are asking the trainees to do. In the example above, the manager of the nutrition department was trained first and had the opportunity to review documentation on the nursing unit prior to the training of the nutritionists. The manager was able to provide encouragement to the group of nutritionists in a way that the physician, clinical documentation specialist, and health information management professional could not.

ASKING FOR NONPHYSICIANS

The asking process of CAMP Method training requires the same kind of qualities in an instructor that the coaching component does. Of primary importance is that the instructor can provide responses to the trainees that they will perceive as credible and helpful. Because they are in an observing mode, asking and coaching are not as critical for managers. Therefore, your development efforts should be focused on asking and coaching primarily for nonphysician clinicians, clinical documentation specialists, and health information management coders.

MASTERING FOR NONPHYSICIANS

Mastering for nonphysicians and nonclinicians is a different two-step process than for physicians. For the clinical documentation specialists and the coders, they first learn the criteria for high quality clinical documentation. Then—unlike physicians who master the documentation process during training—the clinical documentation specialists and coders must master record review, identification of deficiencies, questioning, and management of the response process. Therefore, the initial training included in this book is sufficient for the first step of training those individuals who will be responsible for the clinical documentation review process. However, you will need to create a training program that addresses the other steps in the mastering process consistent with your own internal needs and the CAMP Method components.

CHAPTER SUMMARY

All documentation in the patient record, regardless of the author, should meet the criteria for high quality clinical documentation. The CAMP Method for training was initially developed for physicians. However, the method can be applied universally with minimal modification. A significant body of research, listed in this chapter, has established that self-efficacy, the foundation of the CAMP Method, is also effective in training nonphysician clinicians. Ideally, you should train all caregivers, noncaregivers who document in the medical record, and staff who evaluate the content of the medical record.

You will need to adjust the CAMP Method concepts to each group. For example, for peer learning, you will need to include a member in the instructional team who has a background similar to the group being trained. Mastering, for staff who evaluate the content of the medical record, is a more involved process than physician mastery. The record review staff must learn both the criteria for high quality clinical documentation from the physician training as well as an additional set of skills focused around questioning the physician, obtaining a response, and recording the interaction.

STEPS YOU CAN TAKE TODAY

- Make a list of all individuals in your organization who should receive clinical documentation training.
- Discuss with your colleagues whether your organization has any clinical leaders—like the director of nutrition in this chapter's case study—who, if trained, could play a pivotal role in your clinical documentation program.

13. Best Practices

B EST PRACTICES should be aimed at ensuring that your program has a positive impact on your organization and that the processes and results of the clinical documentation program are in regulatory and legal compliance. Federal and state governments, who fund about one-third of healthcare, have significant resources at stake. As such, they have an interest in ensuring that the money they are paying is for services that were actually performed. Clinical documentation is the basis for payment. Insurers and government entities should feel that your program aims to obtain only the highest quality clinical documentation, which benefits both your organization and the payers. Should questions ever arise, your program methodology is your primary defense that your documentation program is in compliance.

START WITH GOOD RELATIONSHIPS

Relationships between healthcare organization managers, staff, and physicians are the key to the success of every joint endeavor, including a clinical documentation program. If your organization's relationship with its physicians is not positive and productive, you will want to improve the relationship before moving forward. The chance of obtaining support and compliance from physicians who are not supportive of your organization is slim. Investing time and resources in such a venture is not a good expenditure for your organization.

How can you tell if the relationship with your physicians is in need of improvement? In a positive and engaging relationship, physicians:

- Regularly attend organizational meetings
- Are an important part of the leadership of the organization
- Understand and can verbalize the organization's vision or goals
- Participate on organizational teams

If the physicians in your organization do not align with at least three of these criteria, the senior leadership needs to focus first on building better relationships with the physicians before moving full steam ahead with intense clinical documentation training and program implementation. Volume 1 opens with the following example of an organization that had to improve physician–hospital relations before implementing a clinical documentation program. For practical purposes, the activities were streamlined so that, as the executive team was taking actions to show the physicians they were appreciated and respected, they could also prepare the physicians for the upcoming clinical documentation training. This included some discussion about the importance of clinical documentation. Once the physician satisfaction improved, the prior discussions about clinical documentation provided an excellent segue to beginning the training. The case study from volume 1 is repeated below.

CASE STUDY: A STRONG PHYSICIAN–HOSPITAL RELATIONSHIP IS THE BASIS FOR A SUCCESSFUL CLINICAL DOCUMENTATION PROGRAM

Our team had just completed a formal presentation on the benefits of a clinical documentation program to the senior management of a 267-bed suburban hospital. Everyone piled out of the conference room with the exception of the CEO and the CFO. They lingered behind while we dismantled the presentation equipment. They complimented us on the presentation and said they knew there was a problem with the accuracy and completeness of documentation in their medical records. Then the CEO looked me straight in the eyes and said, "I can't go back to my medical staff with another request for their help. This will be the third request I have had for them this year. We just finished a big length of stay initiative. I *want* to do this, but it's just too much for me to ask of them." He believed that, just like with the length of stay initiative, the physicians would feel like he was asking them essentially to "do yet more work, without getting paid for it." The CEO knew their response would be, "Why should we?"; and he couldn't bear to deal with it again in the near future.

The real problem for this hospital was not just the current operational issue of poor documentation in patient records with its resulting negative impact on the organization. Rather, the issue started much higher up the food chain. It began, as it so often does, with the hospital–physician relationship. At this particular hospital, we started with the end goal of obtaining the medical staff's agreement to move forward with a clinical documentation program. But first, to reach that agreement, we spent the next six months repairing a broken relationship. We used concentrated communication exercises with key members of the medical staff, increased investment in training and education, and encouraged revisions of organizational policy regarding medical staff issues. We also spent a lot of time shifting the paradigm of physician responsibilities to the hospital—in return for their admitting privileges—as well as shifting hospital responsibilities to the physicians. In the end, the clinical documentation program was a success and the relationship a better one. But just like any important relationship, unless you consistently cultivate the relationship, it is likely to atrophy over time.

CLEAR VISION

Listed below are examples of some of the more common vision statements found on hospital and healthcare system Web sites:

- To be a standard-setting academic medical center.
- To be the trusted leader in caring for people and advancing health.
- To create a partnership of physicians, hospitals, and communities that will take the lead in giving consumers throughout the region easy access to a fully coordinated range of services extending from prevention to the most advanced care available.
- To be the academic and community-teaching hospitals and physicians of choice with the most distinguished caliber of physician and professional healthcare staff. We will create the highest quality of care.

All of these visions relate to a high quality of clinical documentation. For example, a *standard setting-medical center* would be one that has both excellent documentation and excellent results reporting that stems from the documentation. In addition, *trust* implies that everything about an organization is trustworthy, including the reliability of its data or results reporting—the very information that customers will use to make decisions about the organization. The third vision describes a future with *easy access and a fully coordinated range of services.* This can only be possible if the organization is making planning decisions based upon accurate and reliable data. And the final vision, which is providing the *highest quality of care*, requires that the organization is generating high quality clinical documentation to achieve this.

Your organization needs to develop a specific vision for the clinical documentation function. The vision statement should be the driving force behind the program and should be repeated often. The statement for clinical documentation may be something like, "Mercy Hospital's quality clinical documentation will consistently meet standards for high quality, thereby contributing to the high accuracy rates of our quality measures and reimbursement." The vision statement, by nature, should determine which senior and mid-level managers need to be involved in the operationalization of the program. The vision statement used as an example above involves individuals from quality improvement, finance, and health information management, at a minimum, to assist in realizing the clinical documentation vision.

Communication and Support

The executive team must communicate the vision for the program over and over to managers and the physicians in the organization. The vision provides the operating group with a focused goal for its work. There should never be a question about why the work is being done and what the ultimate goal of the program is. Without the goal constantly guiding the operations team, the likelihood of achieving it is greatly diminished.

The Commonwealth Fund's report states that physicians consistently believe the following six activities will improve patient care:

- Improved teamwork and communication.
- More use of computer technology.
- Better information on best physician specialists and centers.
- Better treatment guidelines for common conditions.
- Having more time to spend with patients.
- Better patient access to preventive care.[1]

In Press Ganey's *Hospital Check-Up Report*, the organization identified the top five priorities for physician satisfaction. In rank order, they are: (1) response of hospital administration, (2) patient care made easier, (3) how administration deals with change, (4) confidence in hospital administration, and (5) communication with hospital administration.[2] Both the research by Press Ganey and The Commonwealth Fund identify communication between the hospital and the medical staff as a significant concern of physicians. Knowing this, the amount of communication around the new effort of clinical documentation should be comprehensive, well thought-out, and efficient. Volume 1 recommends specific actions for carrying out the communications plan about clinical documentation to the medical staff, including who should communicate and how the communication should happen.

Comprehensive Physician Training

Training, the focus of this book, is the number one key to a successful clinical documentation program. And training physicians is the top priority. As discussed earlier, everyone who documents in the patient record, or who reviews the patient record, should be trained in clinical documentation; but the physician comes first. The support and understanding of the medical staff is necessary for the program to be a success. In the past, many organizations believed that they should focus on training their other clinicians, and they hoped the clinicians could persuade the physicians to cooperate. But this inverse approach is destined for failure because the physician is the author of the documentation. The physicians need to begin the process and not be an afterthought.

Tracking and Feedback

Feedback can occur through program-tracking measures, or key metrics, which are essential to retraining. Program metrics may include operational measures like review rate, query rate, and response rate. Metrics may also include results of audits of clinical documentation and the program. Testing can also be used as a regular measure. Testing is a valuable measure to understand the physicians' knowledge base and for compliance purposes. However, it should not be used as the only program metric because it does not include the *application* of the learned skill.

Whatever your metrics are, it is essential to provide feedback to the appropriate physicians or clinicians about any deficiencies you have identified. As Ken Blanchard says, "feedback is the breakfast of champions." This is true for everyone, including physicians. The physicians in the CAMP™ Method study identified feedback about their documentation as one of the most valuable learning activities for them. It is also important to include positive feedback in your conversations with physicians. Feedback that is regular, individualized, and both positive and critical, will engage physicians and help to sustain the program.

Retrain

Once you have identified individual and program weaknesses or deficiencies, you need to retrain based on this information. Organizations with regular, focused follow-up training are more likely to derive continued benefits from their clinical documentation program than organizations that don't. Figure 13.1 depicts the overall best practices that will help to ensure a successful and sustainable clinical documentation program.

OPERATIONAL BEST PRACTICES

Figure 13.2 lists the operational categories for a "best practices" clinical documentation program. For each content area, a brief explanation of the processes and general considerations is listed. The actual best practices are derived from experiences with clinical documentation program implementation, follow-up, and maintenance. There are common elements to best practices across the healthcare industry. However,

Figure 13.1. Best Practices that will Help Ensure a Successful and Sustainable Clinical Documentation Program

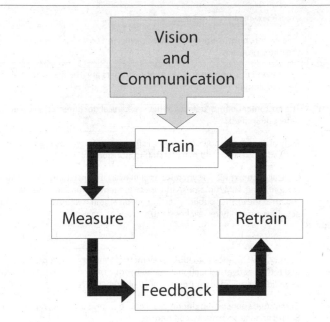

specific organizational characteristics such as the employment status of the medical staff, the types of services provided, and the organizational structure can drive best practices recommendations. Figure 13.2 is provided as general guidance for program operations.

CHAPTER SUMMARY

Every clinical documentation program should continually strive to achieve best practices status. Because of the newness of the function of clinical documentation, best practices criteria are derived from operational as well as regulatory compliance sources. Best practices start with a strong hospital–medical staff relationship and a clear vision for high quality clinical documentation. Continued communication supports a continuous loop of training, measurement, feedback, and retraining to achieve both operational and regulatory compliance best practices status. Finally, an overview of operational best practices, identifying all key activities, individuals, and benchmarks for a successful program is included in this chapter.

Figure 13.2. Program Operations

Content area	Processes within content area
Organization perspective	Clear vision, purpose/program focus, payor, and type of patient care included in the initial program
Program "customers"	Define who the internal and external customers are [the first step in Six Sigma methodology]
Defining "defects"	The customer defines "defects." What is a "clinical documentation defect"? How is a defect quantified?
Structure	Clinical documentation organization chart to explain reporting relationships for both administrative and medical staff responsibilities
Leveraging organizational synergies for clinical documentation success	Clinical documentation synergies exist in most organizations with: medical staff credentialing, HIM functions, UR/case management functions, quality initiatives, HealthGrades/other public reporting, medical staff relationship improvement activities, mortality review, resident/house staff training
Program documentation	Position specifications, including key metrics for success: query policy (concurrent and retrospective); educational manuals; educational activity tracking for program as well as compliance purposes; record of every query
Organizational support	Committee sponsorship during years one, two, and ongoing; reporting to the Board; finance and quality committees
Medical staff support	Physician leadership/ongoing involvement; physician trainers; chain of command for query nonresponses or other problems
Hospitalists' support	Hospitalists can have a central role in the success of clinical documentation
Ancillary clinical support	Engage ancillary clinical staff to support the clinical documentation process: nutrition; wound therapy; respiratory therapy; substance abuse counselors; PAs; nurse practitioners; others
Medical staff strategy	Ongoing activities and education to engage the medical staff in clinical documentation
Tangible tools	For MDs and program staff; hard copy, easily accessible and reproducible; service specific; using the record as a clinical documentation "tool" for training classes and one-on-one training
Software tools	Software should be interfaced with admission/registration system to ensure complete capture of all opportunities; system-wide access to reporting from the software system
Goal setting	Key metrics within the program need to be identified (from the customer's definition of "defects"); goals or targets for each key metric must be set and re-analyzed on a regular basis
Tracking	Use of software to track; tracking policies, procedures, responsibility, and accountability
Measuring	Document the measurement system for consistency and to ensure credibility of the data; use results to retrain and for continuous improvement

Content area	Processes within content area
Reporting	Types of reports, distribution mechanisms; action items, results that are below the target
Monitoring	Day-to-day monitoring and supervision of clinical documentation activities; feedback loop to staff, clinicians, and physicians
Auditing	Regular documentation auditing process, reporting, and follow-up [tie into organization's compliance process]
Continuing education	For medical staff, ancillary clinicians, clinical documentation staff [tie into organization's compliance activities]
Retrospective activities	To ensure 100% capture of all opportunities to improve documentation

STEPS YOU CAN TAKE TODAY

- Review the section entitled "Start with Good Relationships" and determine whether your physicians are involved in the hospital activities noted in the checklist. If not, do you think your physicians are ready to shoulder their responsibility in a clinical documentation program?
- What is your executive team's clear vision for clinical documentation?
- Review the train, measure, feedback, and retrain feedback loop diagram in the section on retraining. How does your program currently incorporate the components in the diagram?

14. Physician–Clinical Documentation Professional Communications

CLINICAL DOCUMENTATION program staff are usually clinicians who have also been trained in correct clinical documentation practices. These clinical documentation professionals (CDPs) are the operational center of the program. They are charged with coordinating training and education activities. In addition, they manage a program's concurrent review process. This involves a CDP reviewing clinical documentation, as close in time as possible to the initial documentation, to identify any documentation that does not meet the established criteria for high quality clinical documentation. The clinical knowledge and status of these individuals is an essential prerequisite for the concurrent verbal query process. Ideally, as physicians are empowered with initial and then continuous follow-up training, the amount of concurrent review necessary should decline because quality is improving. In reality, most organizations are unable to set aside internal resources and/or obtain cooperation from physicians to attend the initial and follow-up training (as described in this book) that is necessary to produce the increase in quality *without* concurrent intervention from clinical documentation professionals. Therefore, concurrent review is likely to remain an important component of every clinical documentation program.

Clinical documentation professionals are a necessary conduit for the initial success, and in many cases for the continued success, of an organization's clinical documentation program. Because CDPs spend a significant amount of time interacting with physicians during both the training and the review process, it is important to ensure the documentation professionals themselves are trained in how to interact with physicians. Because they are clinicians, most CDPs have experience interacting with physicians about clinical issues. However, CDPs should be trained in approach and content regarding their communications with physicians to ensure a compliant and effective program. This chapter addresses the ideal background of a clinical documentation professional, as well as training topics to ensure an effective and compliant program.

THE CLINICAL DOCUMENTATION PROFESSIONAL (CDP)

Clinical documentation is a budding profession. The background and experience of the CDP today is generally in a clinical or health information management discipline. Eventually, the profession will likely have its own academic programs, internships, and certifications. (It appears as though a certification may be currently in the process of being created, at least for the reviewer or specialist role.) In the meantime, we need to rely upon what we know has worked in the thousands of programs implemented, and reimplemented, over the past decade. In general, we know that staff members of a clinical documentation program are more likely to succeed if they have clinical training, record review experience, are well organized, and are comfortable interacting with physicians. Some additional detail is provided below:

Training. In addition to clinical doumentation training, two types of training are essential for a successful CDP: clinical training and coding training. Clinical training is important because the CDP needs to have a good understanding of the disease process, symptoms, the meaning of abnormal test results, medications, and other details included in the patient record. Of critical importance is that the CDP can identify clinical indicators in the patient record that appear to support a diagnosis, or at least be in need of further clarification. This is the basis for identifying documentation that does not meet the criteria for high quality clinical documentation—the key component of the program. Further, because clinical documentation is eventually translated into coded data for reimbursement, quality measures, planning, and research, it is important that the CDP understands the basics of ICD-9-CM and CPT nomenclatures. The coding systems use a certain language that impacts how documentation is translated into a code. It is important for the CDP to be able to determine that a particular mode of documenting may result in a code assignment that misrepresents the patient's diagnosis. The CDP needs coding training to identify these potential deficiencies.

Experience. The CDP should have past experience in the record review process. A CDP must enjoy reviewing records and be *good* at it since record review is the essence of the program. The CDP should also have past experience interacting with physicians and other clinicians. In addition, the CDP should be a good instructor. Although every CDP may not be conducting formal training sessions, every CDP conducts one-on-one instruction with physicians and other clinicians on a regular basis on the nursing units.

Communication skills. The CDP must be at ease communicating with physicians and must be able to manage conflict. Not every encounter will result in conflict, but the ability to negotiate and manage conflict will make the CDP more confident and accomplished. Because many inquiries will be written, the CDP must have good written (as well as verbal) communication skills.

Personality traits. The CDP needs to be well respected by the physicians with whom she interacts. In addition, the CDP should be well organized and goal oriented. Since there is a continuous need to follow-up on inquiries that have been generated until they are resolved, she should also be persistent.

CDP INTERACTION WITH PHYSICIANS SHOULD NOT BE A POTENTIAL COMPLIANCE RISK

If you have trained your physicians and staff members appropriately and implemented the program in accordance with the training guidelines presented in this book, the CDP interaction with physicians should not be a compliance risk. There has been some concern that certain CDP practices such as *leading queries* or *inquiries written on sticky notes* or *the physician's interpretation of the question being asked of her* are compliance risks. Scenarios like the CDP asking the physician if a patient has blood loss anemia, a leading query, are anecdotal examples of potential compliance risks in the interaction between the CDP and the physician. It is unclear whether these scenarios have actually ever occurred, or if they are just worst fears expressed in the form of possible problems. In any event, if your organization has implemented initial and continuous training and a program according to the standardization and criteria provided here, these compliance concerns should never become a reality for you.

The four pillars of compliance are training, policies and procedures, internal monitoring, and regular auditing. Initial and continuous training is an essential part of the clinical documentation program, at least as presented in this book. Policies and procedures were also discussed and are important to the process. Internal monitoring (or the internal documentation audits described in earlier chapters) should be performed by the clinical documentation manager. And finally, an annual audit of your program, whether internal or external, is important as well. As long as you are practicing all of these activities along with the standardized implementation (based on the seven criteria for high quality clinical documentation), you have an excellent insurance policy in place. Figure 14.1 shows the importance of initial training, continuous training, and a standardized program.

Assessing HIM and CDP Relationships with Physicians

Because the relationship between the program staff and the physicians is so important, you may want to have the staff members complete a relationship assessment. Digital copies of the assessment are provided on the accompanying resource disc. Or you can have your staff take the surveys on the CAMP™ Method Web site if you are a subscriber to the service. If you take the survey on the Web site, you will receive an analysis of your results. The assessment questions are provided in figure 14.2 for your review. Following the HIM/CDP assessment, there is also an assessment for hospital managers to rate their relationship with the hospital.

Figure 14.1. Importance of Initial Training, Continuous Training, and a Standardized Program

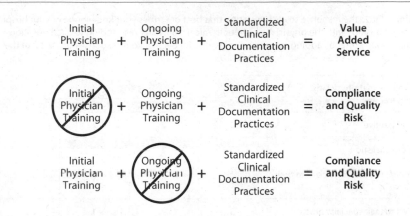

CHAPTER SUMMARY

Because physician interaction is the most important part of the clinical documentation program, your clinical documentation staff should be selected with this requirement in mind. Clinical documentation professionals (CDPs) should have clinical training and experience reviewing records. The CDP should be at ease when communicating with physicians, and she should be goal oriented. If your clinical documentation program incorporates standardized clinical documentation practices, initial physician training and ongoing physician training (consistent with the CAMP Method training), you are providing a value added service to your organization and minimizing compliance risk.

STEPS YOU CAN TAKE TODAY

- Do you have a job description for clinical documentation professionals in your organization? How closely does it resemble the qualifications outlined in the chapter?
- Complete the relationship assessment at the end of the chapter. What areas can you improve regarding your knowledge of, or interaction with, physicians?

Figure 14.2. Hospital–Physician Relationship and HIM/CDP Assessment

Directions: Circle the response to each question that best describes your knowledge of your hospital and its relationships with the physicians on your medical staff. After responding to each question, determine your "score" by adding up the numeric value for each of your responses on part 2 of the survey.

1. I believe that physicians, in general, are:	Often	Sometimes	Rarely	
Competitive	3	2	1	
Individualistic	3	2	1	
Similar to other physicians in their specialty	3	2	1	
Tied to their specialty practice	3	2	1	
#1 TOTAL SCORE	_____	+_____	+_____	=_____

2. How often does your hospital:	Often	Sometimes	Rarely	
Collect detailed information about each physician?	3	2	1	
Analyze patient care data by physician?	3	2	1	
Create opportunities for MDs to participate in hospital activities of their own personal interest?	3	2	1	
#2 TOTAL SCORE	_____	+_____	+_____	=_____

3. How often does your hospital schedule:	Often	Sometimes	Rarely	
Meetings with the medical staff as a whole?	3	2	1	
Meetings with each medical/ surgical specialty?	3	2	1	
Opportunities to "socialize" with physicians?	3	2	1	
Educational programs for physicians?	3	2	1	
#3 TOTAL SCORE	_____	+_____	+_____	=_____

4. How often does your hospital provide physicians with:	Often	Sometimes	Rarely	
"Report cards" comparing their data to others?	3	2	1	
Surveys to learn more about physicians' needs?	3	2	1	
#4 TOTAL SCORE	_____	+_____	+_____	=_____
5. How easy is it for physicians to determine the hospital's:	Very Easy	Somewhat Easy	Not Easy at All	
Mission?	3	2	1	
Values?	3	2	1	
Short-term strategy?	3	2	1	
Long-term strategy?	3	2	1	
#5 TOTAL SCORE	_____	+_____	+_____	=_____
6. How often do the members of the medical staff:	Often	Sometimes	Rarely	
Participate on committees?	3	2	1	
Attend educational opportunities offered by the hospital?	3	2	1	
#6 TOTAL SCORE	_____	+_____	+_____	=_____
7. Does your hospital provide the physicians with:	Yes	No		
Access to medical records in their offices?	3	1		
Value-added HIM services (copies of HIM coding)?	3	1		
A comfortable, welcoming location to complete records?	3	1		
#7 TOTAL SCORE	_____	+_____		=_____

Continues next page

Continued from previous page

8. How would you rate the following in your hospital?:	High	Neutral	Low	
Respect physicians have for Clinical Documentation staff generally	3	2	1	
Respect physicians have for Clinical Documentation reviewers	3	2	1	
Respect physicians have for Clinical Documentation managers	3	2	1	
#8 TOTAL SCORE	_____	+_____	+_____	=_____

15. Operational Challenges of Clinical Documentation and the Electronic Medical Record (EMR): An Overview

THE ELECTRONIC MEDICAL RECORD (EMR) implementation provides a framework for discussion, the sharing of ideas, and an opportunity to extend best practices in clinical documentation into other related areas. One teaching hospital in the Northeast combined the implementation of its clinical documentation program with the EMR implementation. The hospital felt the two teams, documentation and information technology, would create a synergy that could result in happier physicians with more efficient and higher quality documentation. It appears they made a good decision. Template content, in particular, has been complete, compliant, and pleasing to the physicians. In volume 1, we discussed the importance of technology and the knowledge worker providing an organization with a sustainable competitive advantage. The EMR, combined with the skill set of the clinical documenter, provides this same advantage to healthcare organizations. Figure 15.1 demonstrates this concept.

Healthcare organizations are currently in different phases of implementing electronic medical records. Some are just implementing computerized patient order entry (CPOE) while others are rolling out complete EMRs for every care setting. Many organizations have focused initially on implementing the EMR in the outpatient setting. While only a small percentage of hospitals have fully implemented the EMR, we can identify some of the operational challenges that involve clinical documentation.

EMR OPERATIONAL CHALLENGES

Interfaces. Meeting the challenge of interfaces is critical to an effective transformation from the paper medical record to the EMR. Healthcare providers rely on a variety of information systems. Integration of these systems with the EMR can be the key to an effective rollout. Systems include pharmacy, laboratory services, radiology, anesthesia, and a wide variety of specialty software packages that are as unique as the specialists who use them.

Institutions use systems to track findings, trend, analyze the effectiveness of treatments, gather research data, and assess the needs of a variety of patient populations. Individual providers may be resistant to change their methods of gathering data and may feel restricted by the limitations of a new system that is not specifically designed to fit their needs. Attempts to accommodate these needs and to transfer data already collected can be challenging.

Integration with current dictation systems may be necessary, especially during the early phases of transformation. Some specialists may be unable or unwilling to use electronic templates and may insist on continuing to dictate operative reports or consultation letters. Communications methodology within the EMR competes with the current methods that physicians are using to move information quickly, whether it is for lab results, medications and orders, requests for consultation, or for a critically ill or injured patient's past medical history.

Training. Training the variety of users required to implement an EMR is an integral part of a successful implementation. Training needs to be provided for a variety of users, including support staff, administrators, billing staff, internal compliance auditors, HIM personnel, and many levels of clinicians: nurses, physicians, residents, fellows, medical students, physical therapists, nutritionists, social workers, and other mid-level providers.

Training is challenging because of the time and commitment that it requires. Effective training needs to be timed appropriately so users can apply their knowledge shortly after training. This is an extremely time intensive activity and it needs to accommodate a wide variety

Figure 15.1 Importance of Technology and the Knowledge Worker

of computer skill proficiencies. Some users may benefit from group education or online classes, while others need intensive one-on-one attention.

Compliance. Pressure for accuracy of clinical documentation to support the diagnosis and procedure codes is intense. And penalties for inaccuracy are high. Inaccurate claims submissions can result in payer investigations of both institutions and individual providers. Litigation, refunds, and the audit process are time consuming and costly. The EMR is often perceived as a method of enhancing compliance with documentation and coding guidelines.

Despite this, there is increased scrutiny of the EMR, especially by federally funded payers. The volume of documentation is mushrooming with electronic *copy and paste* or *pull-forward* techniques that allow copying information from previous notes or providers' medical record documentation. The ease of creating standard language for teaching physician attestations, consultation language, or a comprehensive physical examination is a great advantage of the EMR. But there is a delicate balance between creating an efficient system and crossing the line where medical record documentation becomes primarily support for high levels of service and the highest reimbursement.

Dropping an accurate bill. Many physicians continue to ask questions like, "Why can't the system choose the codes for me? Will we still need the folks in HIM?" The challenge is that the EMR requires the provider to take greater responsibility for selecting the codes that reflect the services provided. Many providers have relied on support staff to review encounter forms or inpatient billing cards. Providers have access to the entire ICD-9-CM diagnosis codebook but often cannot find codes due to their lack of familiarity with the code *lookups* and the specificity of diagnosis codes available to them.

Physicians are often disappointed that the system will not select their E/M codes based on the elements documented. Although many EMRs have this functionality, it requires the physician to document elements of the exam in specific locations so they can be *counted* by the system logic. Many physicians find this too restricting. There has been much discussion about the accuracy of the calculators as well as the compliance risk associated with inaccurate calculations and attempts to game the system. At an HCCA conference in 2008, a speaker asked the group how many audience members had an EMR with this functionality. Almost everyone in the room, about 200 people, raised their hands. The speaker then asked how many had activated this function; only about 10 hands stayed up.

Design of templates. Whether you are dealing with paper or technology, you can't please everyone when it comes to templates. A template that prompts providers to document the essential elements of a service or procedure is helpful. The EMR allows a variety of options from free text to point-and-click templates where typing is minimal. Some providers will find templates restrictive, while others prefer them. Creating electronic templates may be appealing and may help to get physicians excited about using the EMR. Since many physicians find documentation burdensome, this exercise of creating templates may help engage the providers. The challenge is that templates still require patient-specific information, individualized plans of care, and the description of a unique patient/physician encounter. The EMR will not eliminate the requirement for high quality clinical documentation. For many, especially those with limited computer skills, the EMR increases the burden, at least in the short term.

Quality of care. The EMR can create concerns about conflicting information. For example, there are certain locations for the patient's weight and other vital signs. If the physician decides not to use the locations that are hardwired to capture this information, and instead types them in the progress notes section, the system thinks the note is incomplete and generates a notice. Further, sometimes the templates are not relevant to what the physician is typing. Often, the physician may leave template information on the form that is inconsistent with his own notes, which results in notes that do not make sense. Some of this is a training issue and some of it is the physician taking the time to make the changes.

Physician buy-in. Hospitals who want physician support for EMR implementation need to obtain it by promising the physicians a significant benefit and then delivering on the promise. Here is a situation where the executive team needs to be proactive in obtaining physician support and trust. Without physician cooperation, both treatment and documentation will suffer.

CHAPTER SUMMARY

Implementation of an EMR provides a concurrent opportunity to tackle clinical documentation concerns. Because the EMR is still in its early stages, it is impossible to know all of the operational issues related to both clinical documentation and EMR implementation. However, some of the issues we have seen include: (1) the ability to flawlessly interface clinical documentation between two clinical information systems; (2) the need for extensive, time-consuming education for all users, especially physicians; (3) compliance risks when physicians use *copy and paste* or *pull forward* techniques; (4) the compliant and accurate use of templates; and (5) quality care concerns when the EMR creates conflicting information from different clinician's entries. It is important to be familiar with EMR implementation challenges and ensure that clinical documentation plays a role in the process.

STEPS YOU CAN TAKE TODAY

- Depending on where your organization is in the EMR implementation process, have you encountered any of the challenges noted in the chapter? If not, perhaps you should anticipate them.

16. Clinical Documentation Management: A Dynamic Process

W<small>E EXIST</small> in a constantly changing environment. And healthcare may be impacted by more changes than any other industry. Consequently, it is important to ensure that your clinical documentation program is both standardized and dynamic. In this chapter, we address specific assessment methodologies, outside resources, internal activities, and goal-setting exercises that can ensure your program, and the physicians and staff supporting it, are on the cutting edge of the industry. If you already have an established program, this chapter provides some suggestions on how to breathe new life into it through the training process. If you have a new program, this chapter will help you structure your program to ensure a growing, dynamic documentation function that continues to contribute to your organization's overall vision and mission.

Figure 16.1 demonstrates how a clinical documentation program can be both standardized and receptive to program feedback and changes in the industry, an essential component of any successful clinical documentation program. All of the components illustrated in the graphic are essential to success. First, your organization establishes a vision, communicates it, and practices continuous communication about the program. Second, you standardize the program by using the accepted criteria for high quality clinical documentation as the basis of all training and program operations. Third, you begin the training–feedback loop that will become an ongoing part of your clinical documentation process. Each component of the training loop is described in the chapter on best practices in clinical documentation.

KEEPING EVERYONE ENGAGED

Engaged physicians and employees are committed, hardworking, and passionate about what they do.[1] There is clear evidence that the level of employee engagement correlates to individual, group, and organizational performance.[2] When a new program is implemented, employees tend to be more excited. But organizations often confuse this excitement for engagement, and they assume that the engagement will continue long after the newness wears off. Similarly, when employees join an organization, they're usually enthusiastic, committed, and ready to be advocates for their new employer. Simply put, they're highly engaged. But that first year on the job is often their best. Gallup Organization research reveals that the longer an employee stays with a company, the less engaged she becomes. This drop in productivity presents a significant cost to organizations in terms of profitability and customer satisfaction.[3] In order to maintain high levels of engagement, the collective research on employee engagement should be consulted. Gallup, Towers Perrin, BlessingWhite, and the Corporate Leadership Council have conducted extensive research on employee engagement. Each came up with a list of 12 to 24 elements conducive to long-term employee engagement. Among the various lists, there were eight common elements of employee engagement:

- *Trust and integrity*. How well do managers communicate and "walk the talk"?
- *Nature of the job*. Is it mentally stimulating day-to-day?
- *Line of sight between employee performance and company performance*. Does the employee understand how her work contributes to the company's performance?
- *Career growth opportunities*. Are there future opportunities for growth?
- *Pride about the company*. How much self-esteem does the employee feel by being associated with the company?

Figure 16.1. How a Clinical Documentation Program can be Both Standardized and Dynamic

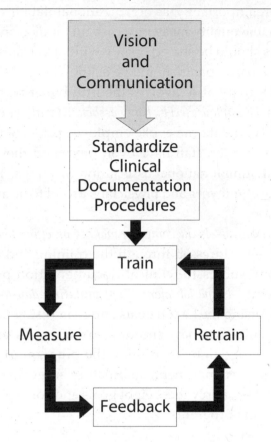

- *Coworkers/team members.* Do they significantly influence an employee's level of engagement?
- *Employee development.* Is the company making an effort to develop the employee's skills?
- *Relationship with one's manager.* Does the employee value his relationship with his manager?[4]

This list suggests some basic activities that can increase the likelihood of sustained employee and physician engagement in a clinical documentation program. Some of these concepts are easier to put into practice than others. For example, you can achieve the third bullet point—*Does the employee understand how her work contributes to the organization's performance?*—through continuous program metrics and feedback. More importantly, as organizational data is converted into publicly available quality measures, case mix index, and severity, the improvements should be shared openly with physicians and program staff, and these participants should be acknowledged for their contributions. This activity also involves the fifth bullet point—*How much self-esteem does the employee feel by being associated with the company?* High quality ratings and data can evoke employee pride. Some physician–clinical documentation staff have even presented their programs as case studies at annual national association meetings. These kinds of activities make employees and physicians proud to be associated with the organization.

The seventh point—*Is the company making an effort to develop the employee's skills?*—is addressed through the training and feedback loop essential to any successful clinical documentation program. Even the second point—*Is the job mentally stimulating day-to-day?*—can be addressed by raising the bar on goals and reassessing the program vision. Some organizations have encouraged employees' and physicians' interest in the program by expanding the program to new locations like the emergency department, ambulatory surgery, and clinics. For sustainable success, apply these eight goals and concepts to your clinical documentation program.

Physicians
The basics

When trying to obtain the support and involvement of physicians, we often overlook the basics. But physicians, like anyone else, want to work where they are respected, cultivated, appreciated, and thanked for their efforts. Often the only feedback physicians receive from hospitals is critical, such as when they have done something inconsistent with hospital policies. In an informal survey some physicians revealed that the only time they got a letter or other communication from the hospital was to let them know how many uncompleted delinquent records they had in the medical record department that needed to be updated. You need to proactively communicate positive information to your physicians; even a simple thank you for their cooperation can make a difference. And acknowledging when their documentation is consistent with high quality standards—instead of contacting them only when there are deficiencies in their documentation—can make a difference in how they view you and the organization. One hospital CEO, when briefed by the clinical documentation team on the details of the new program, asked why the hospital didn't have an *'atta boy!* sticker to put on patient records when physicians did a particularly good job of documenting. As you can probably guess, this was an organization that had great hospital–physician relationships because they were cultivated from the top. Taking action on respecting, cultivating, appreciating, and thanking physicians can change a negative and unsupportive attitude into one that is both positive and full of support—in other words, an engaged physician.

Involvement

After you have mastered the basics, the next step is physician involvement. You won't be able to involve every member of your medical staff, but take advantage of the ones who are interested in participating. Because some physicians who are interested may not step up to participate without being asked, offer many opportunities for physicians to volunteer. The more involvement they have in the program, the more the program becomes their own. Since physicians are the authors of the documentation that is our primary concern, we want them to feel that they "own" the clinical documentation program. Physicians should not be responsible for administrating it, but they should take ownership of the vision and the program goals. This will only happen if physicians are involved by having their suggestions implemented into the program. If their suggestions are successful, you are likely to see more engagement from the physicians who were involved with the program, and the group will grow. In one academic medical center, three physicians saw the clinical documentation program as an opportunity for them to learn and research so that they could write a paper for publication in an academic journal. The recognition of their peers motivated them to engage in the program.

Other Clinicians

Other clinicians—nurse practitioners, physician assistants, nutritionists, and therapists—also need to stay engaged. Recognition, while an important element for clinicians, can be challenging to measure. You should add a measure into your program metrics that accounts for the contributions of clinicians. For example, if you can show a significant decline in the number of queries required for a type of malnutrition, this may be a reason to award or recognize the nutrition staff. Or perhaps you can show a decline in queries to cardiologists. If cardiology physician assistants are an important component of getting the cardiologists to respond, then you can recognize the cardiology staff. But recognition is only one part of the process of continuous engagement. Individualized feedback, along with continuous, specific training, is also important. The individualized feedback may need to be tied in with the clinician's service or with testing instruments. Providing education after the initial training will have a positive impact on employee engagement.

Program Staff

Of the eight common components of employee engagement noted above, the eighth component—*Does the employee value her relationship with her manager?*—may be the most important for the clinical documentation program staff. The manager for this group will play a significant role in continued engagement. You need to choose wisely and ensure that, at least in the beginning, the interaction between the managers and program staff is either monitored or discussed among the managers, program staff, and the senior executive to whom they report.

It is essential that clinical documentation program staff members are continuously engaged. This may be the most challenging group for engagement because the implementation of a new program is stressful and time consuming. For this group, you need to manage them away from burnout and towards a continuous positive focus for the program. Their ability to continue to build positive relationships with all of the physicians is important not only for physician engagement, but also for the program staff. Recognition is helpful. Allowing the clinical documentation staff to be involved in creating new components of the program, such as retraining, can be a very positive activity, especially if this activity can be done in groups.

CONTINUOUS TRAINING

It is important to provide ongoing clinical documentation training. As figure 16.1 shows, training should never end. But it can be challenging for organizations to find either the economic support or the motivation to continue the training. One organization's solution was to combine clinical documentation training with compliance training. At first the CEO of the organization felt that the two topics were not congruent; however, the quarterly training and testing proved to be synergistic. Physicians were already used to completing quarterly compliance training. Now, the compliance and clinical documentation training slide shows included 10 to 12 slides, and 5 to 7 multiple choice questions. Though the physicians viewed one online training program and took one quarterly test, they received two test scores, one for compliance and one for clinical documentation.

Policies and Procedures

As your program matures, you should develop detailed, easy to apply policies and procedures. If managed appropriately, this is also an activity that can be used to engage your staff. One academic medical center in the Northeast used the development of clinical documentation policies and procedures to engage the physicians in the organization. The organization began what seemed to be a tedious process by slicing up policies and procedures into 18 different service types. The clinical documentation program staff had developed general policies and procedures that would be used as the basis for standardization of all policies and procedures. But both the clinical documentation professionals and the health information coders found that there were different issues with different services, and they needed a comprehensive manual for reference. The CMO easily gathered volunteers from each service; in fact, some services offered two or three physicians to help with the process. These physicians met on a monthly basis for six months with a subgroup of coders and clinical documentation professionals to develop policies for each specialty. The result was al-most 800 pages of policies and procedures. The document provided the resource that everyone had been seeking. It increased their confidence in the work they were doing. Furthermore, the process of developing the procedures increased engagement. When the policies and proce-dures were ultimately finalized and put into use, everyone involved was proud of the accomplishment.

CHAPTER SUMMARY

Continuous review and improvement is an essential component of any clinical documentation program. Your program should be both stan-dardized and dynamic. Standardization ensures that your organization remains compliant and consistent in its application of the principles and faithful to the laws and regulations related to clinical documenta-tion. A dynamic process in clinical documentation is one that ensures continuous measurement, feedback, and retraining. A dynamic process helps to ensure continuous improvement, high quality, and increased employee and physician engagement.

It is important to keep everyone engaged, but physicians most of all. To lay the groundwork for physician engagement, start with the basics: appreciate, respect, cultivate, and thank them. Then involve them in the process to the point where they feel like they own it, as they should. Consider involving physicians in the policy and procedure develop-ment. Having them contribute to the design of policies and procedures is certain to increase physician engagement. Your program will thrive with the continued engagement of physicians, other clinicians, and your program staff.

STEPS YOU CAN TAKE TODAY

- Talk with your colleagues about how your organization has ensured standardization of its clinical documentation program.
- Review the eight key drivers of employee engagement. How would you rate your physicians, clinicians, and program staff regarding

their engagement in your clinical documentation program?
- If you don't already have one in place, institute a *thank you policy* for physicians who consistently provide high quality documentation.

Appendix:

Testing Instruments Used in CAMP Training

Clinical Documentation Self-Efficacy Questionnaire

Please respond to each question by circling the number that best corresponds to your feelings.

	Poor	Fair	Good	Very Good	Excellent
1. How would you rate the quality of your clinical documentation?	0	1	2	3	4
2. For my patients, I am confident that I can document in a hospital record:	Not at all	A little	Somewhat	Mostly	Completely
a. legibly	0	1	2	3	4
b. a complete patient history and physical	0	1	2	3	4
c. a history and physical within 24 hours of admission	0	1	2	3	4
d. all of the patient's chronic conditions	0	1	2	3	4
e. all of the patient's acute conditions	0	1	2	3	4
f. the clinical significance of an abnormal diagnostic test	0	1	2	3	4
g. the patient's diagnosis as interpreted on radiology reports	0	1	2	3	4
h. the patient's diagnosis as interpreted on a path report	0	1	2	3	4
i. the patient's diagnosis in the progress notes before discharge	0	1	2	3	4
j. the patient's discharge summary within 3 days of discharge	0	1	2	3	4

3. I am confident that I can document the etiology or possible etiology of a symptom for a patient who presents with:	Not at all	A little	Somewhat	Mostly	Completely
a. chest pain	0	1	2	3	4
b. abdominal pain	0	1	2	3	4
c. shortness of breath	0	1	2	3	4
d. syncope	0	1	2	3	4
e. vertigo	0	1	2	3	4
4. I am confident that I can document the clinical significance of an abnormal:	Not at all	A little	Somewhat	Mostly	Completely
a. lab test	0	1	2	3	4
b. EKG	0	1	2	3	4
c. X-ray	0	1	2	3	4
d. CT scan	0	1	2	3	4
e. culture & sensitivity	0	1	2	3	4
f. echocardiogram	0	1	2	3	4
5. I am confident that I can document patient diagnoses in a way that will:	Not at all	A little	Somewhat	Mostly	Completely
a. allow the hospital coder to accurately code the patient's diagnoses	0	1	2	3	4
b. meet Medicare documentation requirements	0	1	2	3	4
c. meet Joint Commission documentation requirements	0	1	2	3	4
	Poor	Fair	Good	Very Good	Excellent
6. Overall, how would you rate the quality of your clinical documentation?	0	1	2	3	4

7. What do you consider to be your strengths when it comes to clinical documentation?

_____

_____

8. What do you consider to be your weaknesses when it comes to clinical documentation?

_____

_____

9. What do you believe facilitates good clinical documentation?

_____

_____

10. What do you believe are barriers to good clinical documentation?

_____

_____

11. What are your suggestions for improving physicians' clinical documentation?

_____

_____

Clinical Documentation Attitudes and Opinions Survey

Directions: Read each statement and circle the number that most closely describes your belief:

I believe that my clinical documentation in a patient's hospital record impacts:	Not at all	Very little	Not sure	Somewhat	A great deal
a. The patient's quality of care overall	0	1	2	3	4
b. My medical malpractice exposure	0	1	2	3	4
c. My "report card" or other public data profiles which detail my medical practices	0	1	2	3	4
d. Medicare Quality Indicators	0	1	2	3	4
e. Joint Commission (JCAHO) accreditation	0	1	2	3	4
f. The treatment the patient receives from other caregivers	0	1	2	3	4
g. Healthcare planning	0	1	2	3	4
h. The follow-up care received by the patient	0	1	2	3	4
i. Medical research	0	1	2	3	4
j. Healthcare policy decisions	0	1	2	3	4
k. Quality improvement projects	0	1	2	3	4
l. The payment the hospital receives for the care delivered	0	1	2	3	4
m. The payment I receive for the care delivered	0	1	2	3	4
I believe that:	Definitely disagree	Disagree somewhat	Not sure	Agree somewhat	Definitely agree
a. Clinical documentation is important	0	1	2	3	4

I believe that:	Definitely disagree	Disagree somewhat	Not sure	Agree somewhat	Definitely agree
b. It is important for physicians to support the hospital's needs	0	1	2	3	4
c. There is a relationship between the documentation I provide on a patient's hospital record and the patient's office record	0	1	2	3	4
d. The government's role in healthcare is necessary	0	1	2	3	4
e. Healthcare providers should comply with government regulations	0	1	2	3	4
f. Feedback about documentation practices is helpful	0	1	2	3	4
g. The use of templates improves clinical documentation	0	1	2	3	4
h. Good documentation should be recognized via monetary rewards	0	1	2	3	4
i. Good documentation should be acknowledged publicly	0	1	2	3	4
j. The opinions of medical staff leaders impact physician behavior	0	1	2	3	4
k. It is important to have a positive hospital-physician relationship	0	1	2	3	4
l. The use of an electronic medical record results in improved documentation in the patient's record	0	1	2	3	4
m. Dictating progress notes results in improved documentation	0	1	2	3	4
n. The use of checklists improves clinical documentation	0	1	2	3	4

Please rate the value of the clinical documentation training you received from the following sources. If you did not receive any training from a listed source, circle the number "0" that corresponds to "none."	None	Poor	Below Average	Average	Above Average	Excellent
a. Medical school	0	1	2	3	4	5
b. Prior residency programs	0	1	2	3	4	5
c. The AMA	0	1	2	3	4	5
d. A formal documentation improvement program	0	1	2	3	4	5
e. The Internet	0	1	2	3	4	5
f. Videotapes	0	1	2	3	4	5
g. Audiotapes	0	1	2	3	4	5
h. The hospital's compliance officer	0	1	2	3	4	5
i. The hospital's HIM/medical record department	0	1	2	3	4	5
j. Seminars I have attended	0	1	2	3	4	5
k. The hospital's clinical documentation staff	0	1	2	3	4	5

Have you ever received an inquiry to clarify your documentation in an inpatient medical record?

❑ Yes

Specify type of inquiry_____

❑ No

Overall, how would you rate the quality of your clinical documentation?

❑ Poor   ❑ Fair   ❑ Good   ❑ Very Good   ❑ Excellent

Clinical Documentation Test and Assessment

Part 1: Circle the best answer for each of the multiple choice questions below.

1. Physician documentation in patient records is translated into ICD-9-CM codes. These codes are used to:

    a. rank a hospital's quality of care by organizations such as HealthGrades.com
    b. determine the amount of reimbursement a hospital will receive for patient care
    c. direct healthcare planning and research activities
    d. all of the above

2. A patient's H&P should be documented and available on the patient's record:

    a. at the time of admission
    b. within 24 hours of admission
    c. within 48 hours of admission
    d. by the time of discharge

3. One illegible progress note in a patient's record:

    a. will not have any impact on the patient's care as long as the other notes are legible
    b. will be interpreted based upon the other documentation and test results on the same day
    c. will be treated as though no care was provided on that day
    d. can negatively impact patient care, medical malpractice defense, and reimbursement for the care
    e. both c & d

4. Clinical documentation in an inpatient record can only be translated into an ICD-9-CM code if it is documented by a:

    a. board certified physician
    b. licensed, treating physician
    c. primary care practitioner
    d. consulting physician

Part 2: Document the diagnoses for the patient scenarios described below.

A. A patient is admitted with abdominal pain and nausea and vomiting. Initial and subsequent lab tests reveal a sodium of 120 and 121. The patient is placed on normal saline 120cc/hr. Document the patient's diagnoses.

_____

_____

_____

B. You are following a patient post-surgically with a fem-pop bypass. During surgery, the patient lost 300cc of blood. The patient's post-surgical hgb and hct dropped from 13 and 24 to 10 and 21. The patient received 2U of packed red blood cells after surgery. Document any post-operative diagnosis (es) that these lab results and treatment may represent.

_____

_____

_____

C. A patient's urine C&S reveals >100,000 colonies of E. coli and the patient is placed on bactrim. Document any diagnosis that this lab finding and treatment may represent.

_____

_____

_____

D. A patient with pneumonia per chest X-ray has sputum C&S findings of gram negative rods, too numerous to count. Document any diagnosis that this finding may represent.

_____

_____

_____

E. A patient admitted with atrial fibrillation has echocardiogram results of moderate mitral regurgitation and aortic sclerosis. Document any diagnoses these findings may represent.

_____

_____

_____

F. A patient admitted with dehydration has a chest X-ray positive for COPD. Document any diagnoses these findings may represent.

_____

_____

_____

G. A patient is admitted for cardiac catheterization to rule out suspected CAD. The patient has a history of CHF and needs to be placed on Lasix. Document the order for Lasix for this patient.

_____

_____

_____

H. You are following a surgical patient with DM Type II. After surgery the patient's blood glucose reaches 290 and the patient is placed on sliding scale insulin. Document any diagnosis that this finding and treatment may represent.

_____

_____

_____

I. A patient is admitted with chest pain. EGD performed after admission shows GERD. Document any diagnoses that these findings may represent.

_____

_____

_____

J. A patient is admitted with syncope. EKG shows bradycardia. Document any diagnoses that these findings may represent.

_____

_____

_____

K. A patient's EKG is documented with several runs of V-tach. Document any diagnoses that these findings may represent.

_____

_____

_____

Clinical Documentation Test and Assessment Answer Key

Answer Key
Total points: 71

Note: words in italics denote the specific concept of clinical documentation being tested in the question.

Part 1: Multiple Choice
[4 points each]

1. d *completeness*
2. b *timeliness*
3. e *legibility*
4. b *clarity*

Part 2: Document the diagnoses for the patient scenarios described below
[5 points each. 4 points each for content. 1 point each for legibility.]

A. Hyponatremia *clarity; legibility*
B. Acute (1 point) blood loss (2 points) anemia (1 point) *precision; completeness; legibility*
C. Urinary tract infection (3 points) due to E. coli (1 point) *precision; completeness; legibility*
D. Gram negative pneumonia *precision; clarity; legibility*
E. Mitral valve regurgitation (2 points) Aortic sclerosis (2 points) *clarity; completeness; legibility*
F. COPD *clarity; completeness; legibility*
G. Lasix for CHF *clarity; legibility*
H. Uncontrolled DM II *precision; completeness; legibility*
I. Chest pain due to GERD *clarity*
J. Syncope due to bradycardia *clarity; legibility*
K. Ventricular tachycardia *clarity; completeness; legibility*

Clinical Documentation Training Evaluation

Thank you for participating in this clinical documentation training program. Please complete this post-session evaluation and tell us the degree to which you believe the program met its objectives.

How do you think the training session enabled you to meet the following objectives?:

	Not at all	A little	Somewhat	Mostly	Completely
1. Understand the relationship between physician documentation and the translation of that documentation into ICD-9-CM coded data	0	1	2	3	4
2. Understand that ICD-9-CM coded data is used for planning, reimbursement, quality ratings, Medicare Conditions of Participation, JCAHO Core Measures, and research	0	1	2	3	4
3. Document in the patient record:	**Not at all**	**A little**	**Somewhat**	**Mostly**	**Completely**
a. timely	0	1	2	3	4
b. legibly	0	1	2	3	4
c. completely	0	1	2	3	4
d. clearly	0	1	2	3	4
e. unambiguously	0	1	2	3	4
f. precisely	0	1	2	3	4
4. Document	**Not at all**	**A little**	**Somewhat**	**Mostly**	**Completely**
a. detail and precision in the patient's principal diagnosis	0	1	2	3	4
b. all chronic co-existing secondary diagnoses	0	1	2	3	4
c. all acute co-existing secondary diagnoses	0	1	2	3	4

4. Document	Not at all	A little	Somewhat	Mostly	Completely
d. the clinical significance of all abnormal diagnostic tests	0	1	2	3	4
e. the etiology or suspected etiology of symptoms	0	1	2	3	4

5. Do you believe the	Not at all	A little	Somewhat	Mostly	Completely
a. practice exercises were helpful?	0	1	2	3	4
b. facilitator was organized in presentation?	0	1	2	3	4
c. facilitator gave good examples?	0	1	2	3	4
d. video was helpful?	0	1	2	3	4
e. the opportunity for discussion was helpful?	0	1	2	3	4

6. What did you find most helpful?

_____

_____

7. What did you find least helpful?

_____

_____

8. What are your suggestions for improving the session?

_____

_____

Hospital–Physician Relationship — Clinical Documentation Staff Assessment, Part I

Directions: Circle the response to each question that best describes your knowledge of your hospital and its relationships with the physicians on your medical staff. After responding to each question, determine your "score" by adding up the numeric value for each of your responses on part 2 of the survey.

1. I believe that physicians, in general, are:	Often	Sometimes	Rarely	
Competitive	3	2	1	
Individualistic	3	2	1	
Similar to other physicians in their specialty	3	2	1	
Tied to their specialty practice	3	2	1	
#1 TOTAL SCORE	_____	+_____	+_____	=_____

2. How often does your hospital:	Often	Sometimes	Rarely	
Collect detailed information about each physician?	3	2	1	
Analyze patient care data by physician?	3	2	1	
Create opportunities for MDs to participate in hospital activities of their own personal interest?	3	2	1	
#2 TOTAL SCORE	_____	+_____	+_____	=_____

3. How often does your hospital schedule:	Often	Sometimes	Rarely	
Meetings with the medical staff as a whole?	3	2	1	
Meetings with each medical/ surgical specialty?	3	2	1	
Opportunities to "socialize" with physicians?	3	2	1	
Educational programs for physicians?	3	2	1	
#3 TOTAL SCORE	_____	+_____	+_____	=_____

4. How often does your hospital provide physicians with:	Often	Sometimes	Rarely	
"Report cards" comparing their data to others?	3	2	1	
Surveys to learn more about physicians' needs?	3	2	1	
#4 TOTAL SCORE	_____	+_____	+_____	=_____

5. How easy is it for physicians to determine the hospital's:	Very Easy	Somewhat Easy	Not Easy at All	
Mission?	3	2	1	
Values?	3	2	1	
Short-term strategy?	3	2	1	
Long-term strategy?	3	2	1	
#5 TOTAL SCORE	_____	+_____	+_____	=_____

6. How often do the members of the medical staff:	Often	Sometimes	Rarely	
Participate on committees?	3	2	1	
Attend educational opportunities offered by the hospital?	3	2	1	
#6 TOTAL SCORE	_____	+_____	+_____	=_____

7. Does your hospital provide the physicians with:	Yes	No		
Access to medical records in their offices?	3	1		
Value-added HIM services (copies of HIM coding)?	3	1		
A comfortable, welcoming location to complete records?	3	1		
#7 TOTAL SCORE	_____	+_____		=_____

8. How would you rate the following in your hospital?:	High	Neutral	Low	
Respect physicians have for Clinical Documentation staff generally	3	2	1	
Respect physicians have for Clinical Documentation reviewers	3	2	1	
Respect physicians have for Clinical Documentation managers	3	2	1	
#8 TOTAL SCORE	_____	+_____	+_____	=_____

Hospital–Physician Relationship Assessment, Part II

Directions: For each section in the H–P Relationship Assessment, calculate your total score and insert the score into column D on the table below. Column E contains the minimum recommended score for each section of the assessment. In column F, check any sections where your score (in column D) is *less than* the minimum recommended score in Column E. Focus your development efforts on these activities.

A	B	C	D	E	F
Sec	Topic	Total possible points	Your score	Minimum*	Need to improve
1	Knowledge of physicians as a group	12		10	
2	Knowing each physician	9		9	
3	Formal communication	12		10	
4	Informal communication	6		5	
5	Hospital's "culture clarity"	12		10	
6	Physician support for hospital activities	6		5	
7	"Serving" your physicians	9		8	
8	Respect and communication	9		8	

* Minimum score recommended to provide a strong basis for strong current and continuing physician–hospital relationship building.

Hospital–Physician Relationship —
Health Information Management Assessment, Part I

Directions: Circle the response to each question that best describes your knowledge of your hospital and its relationships with the physicians on your medical staff. After responding to each question, determine your "score" by adding up the numeric value for each of your responses on part 2 of the survey.

1. I believe that physicians, in general, are:	Often	Sometimes	Rarely	
Competitive	3	2	1	
Individualistic	3	2	1	
Similar to other physicians in their specialty	3	2	1	
Tied to their specialty practice	3	2	1	
#1 TOTAL SCORE	_____	+_____	+_____	=_____
2. How often does your hospital:	Often	Sometimes	Rarely	
Collect detailed information about each physician?	3	2	1	
Analyze patient care data by physician?	3	2	1	
Create opportunities for MDs to participate in hospital activities of their own personal interest?	3	2	1	
#2 TOTAL SCORE	_____	+_____	+_____	=_____
3. How often does your hospital schedule:	Often	Sometimes	Rarely	
Meetings with the medical staff as a whole?	3	2	1	
Meetings with each medical/surgical specialty?	3	2	1	
Opportunities to "socialize" with physicians?	3	2	1	
Educational programs for physicians?	3	2	1	
#3 TOTAL SCORE	_____	+_____	+_____	=_____

4. How often does your hospital provide physicians with:	Often	Sometimes	Rarely	
"Report cards" comparing their data to others?	3	2	1	
Surveys to learn more about physicians' needs?	3	2	1	
#4 TOTAL SCORE	_____	+_____	+_____	=_____

5. How easy is it for physicians to determine the hospital's:	Very Easy	Somewhat Easy	Not Easy at All	
Mission?	3	2	1	
Values?	3	2	1	
Short-term strategy?	3	2	1	
Long-term strategy?	3	2	1	
#5 TOTAL SCORE	_____	+_____	+_____	=_____

6. How often do the members of the medical staff:	Often	Sometimes	Rarely	
Participate on committees?	3	2	1	
Attend educational opportunities offered by the hospital?	3	2	1	
#6 TOTAL SCORE	_____	+_____	+_____	=_____

7. Does your hospital provide the physicians with:	Yes	No		
Access to medical records in their offices?	3	1		
Value-added HIM services (copies of HIM coding)?	3	1		
A comfortable, welcoming location to complete records?	3	1		
#7 TOTAL SCORE	_____	+_____		=_____

8. How would you rate the following in your hospital?:	High	Neutral	Low	
Respect physicians have for HIM staff generally	3	2	1	
Respect physicians have for HIM coders	3	2	1	
Respect physicians have for HIM managers	3	2	1	
#8 TOTAL SCORE	_____	+_____	+_____	=_____

Hospital–Physician Relationship Assessment, Part II

Directions: For each section in the H–P Relationship Assessment, calculate your total score and insert the score into column D on the table below. Column E contains the minimum recommended score for each section of the assessment. In column F, check any sections where your score (in column D) is *less than* the minimum recommended score in Column E. Focus your development efforts on these activities.

A	B	C	D	E	F
Sec	Topic	Total possible points	Your score	Minimum*	Need to improve
1	Knowledge of physicians as a group	12		10	
2	Knowing each physician	9		9	
3	Formal communication	12		10	
4	Informal communication	6		5	
5	Hospital's "culture clarity"	12		10	
6	Physician support for hospital activities	6		5	
7	"Serving" your physicians	9		8	
8	Respect and communication	9		8	

* Minimum score recommended to provide a strong basis for strong current and continuing physician–hospital relationship building.

Hospital–Physician Relationship — Senior Manager Assessment, Part I

Directions: Circle the response to each question that best describes your knowledge of your hospital and its relationships with the physicians on your medical staff. After responding to each question, determine your "score" by adding up the numeric value for each of your responses on part 2 of the survey.

1. I believe that physicians, in general, are:	Often	Sometimes	Rarely	
Competitive	3	2	1	
Individualistic	3	2	1	
Similar to other physicians in their specialty	3	2	1	
Tied to their specialty practice	3	2	1	
#1 TOTAL SCORE	_____	+_____	+_____	=_____

2. How often does your hospital:	Often	Sometimes	Rarely	
Collect detailed information about each physician?	3	2	1	
Analyze patient care data by physician?	3	2	1	
Create opportunities for MDs to participate in hospital activities of their own personal interest?	3	2	1	
#2 TOTAL SCORE	_____	+_____	+_____	=_____

3. How often does your hospital schedule:	Often	Sometimes	Rarely	
Meetings with the medical staff as a whole?	3	2	1	
Meetings with each medical/ surgical specialty?	3	2	1	
Opportunities to "socialize" with physicians?	3	2	1	
Educational programs for physicians?	3	2	1	
#3 TOTAL SCORE	_____	+_____	+_____	=_____

4. How often does your hospital provide physicians with:	Often	Sometimes	Rarely	
"Report cards" comparing their data to others?	3	2	1	
Surveys to learn more about physicians' needs?	3	2	1	
#4 TOTAL SCORE	_____	+_____	+_____	=_____

5. How easy is it for physicians to determine the hospital's:	Very Easy	Somewhat Easy	Not Easy at All	
Mission?	3	2	1	
Values?	3	2	1	
Short-term strategy?	3	2	1	
Long-term strategy?	3	2	1	
#5 TOTAL SCORE	_____	+_____	+_____	=_____

6. How often do the members of the medical staff:	Often	Sometimes	Rarely	
Participate on committees?	3	2	1	
Attend educational opportunities offered by the hospital?	3	2	1	
#6 TOTAL SCORE	_____	+_____	+_____	=_____

7. Does your hospital provide the physicians with:	Yes	No		
Access to medical records in their offices?	3	1		
Value-added HIM services (copies of HIM coding)?	3	1		
A comfortable, welcoming location to complete records?	3	1		
#7 TOTAL SCORE	_____	+_____		=_____

8. How would you rate the following in your hospital?:	High	Neutral	Low	
Respect physicians have for hospital senior managers	3	2	1	
Respect physicians have for hospital middle managers	3	2	1	
Respect hospital managers have for physicians	3	2	1	
#8 TOTAL SCORE	_____	+_____	+_____	=_____

Hospital–Physician Relationship Assessment, Part II

Directions: For each section in the H–P Relationship Assessment, calculate your total score and insert the score into column D on the table below. Column E contains the minimum recommended score for each section of the assessment. In column F, check any sections where your score (in column D) is *less than* the minimum recommended score in Column E. Focus your development efforts on these activities.

A	B	C	D	E	F
Sec	Topic	Total possible points	Your score	Minimum*	Need to improve
1	Knowledge of physicians as a group	12		10	
2	Knowing each physician	9		9	
3	Formal communication	12		10	
4	Informal communication	6		5	
5	Hospital's "culture clarity"	12		10	
6	Physician support for hospital activities	6		5	
7	"Serving" your physicians	9		8	
8	Respect and communication	9		8	

* Minimum score recommended to provide a strong basis for strong current and continuing physician–hospital relationship building.

Endnotes

INTRODUCTION

1. Based on informal, convenience sample surveys performed during *7 Steps to Your Best Possible Healthcare* training sessions by Ruthann Russo, 2007–2008.

2. Ruthann Russo, "Improving Self-Efficacy and Organizational Performance," (PhD diss., Touro University International, 2007), 206.

3. A. J. Audet, M. M. Doty, J. Shamasdin, and S. C. Schoenbaum, *Physicians' View on Quality of Care: Findings from The Commonwealth Fund National Survey of Physicians and Quality of Care* (New York: The Commonwealth Fund, 2005).

CHAPTER 1

1. Criteria were derived, in part, from the following sources: AHIMA Coding Products and Services Team, "Managing and Improving Data Quality" (AHIMA Practice Brief), *Journal of AHIMA* 74, no. 7 (2003): 64A–C; Centers for Disease Control, *Official Guidelines for Coding and Reporting* (Washington, D.C.: U.S. Department of Health and Human Services, 2005); Joint Commission on the Accreditation of Healthcare Organizations, *Comprehensive Accreditation Manual for Hospitals: The Official Handbook* (Chicago: Joint Commisssion Resources, 2006); and Centers for Medicare and Medicaid Services, *Medicare Conditions of Participation* (Code of Federal Regulations, Title 42, vol. 4, 2005).

2. See A. Bandura, "Self-Efficacy Mechanism in Human Agency," *American Psychologist* 37, no. 2 (1982): 122–47 and A. Bandura, "Self-Efficacy: Toward a Unifying Theory of Behavioral Change," *Psychological Review* 84, no. 2 (1977): 191–215.

3. A. D. Stajkovic and F. Luthans, "Self-Efficacy and Work-Related Performances: A Meta-Analysis," *Psychological Bulletin* 124 (1998): 240–61.

4. H. B. Simmons and M. A. Goldberg, *Charting the Cost of Inaction* (2003); available online at: *www.nchc.org/materials/studies/Cost_of_Inaction_Full_Report.pdf*.

5. See B. M. Cascio, J. H. Wilckens, M. C. Ain, C. Toulson, and F. J. Frassica, "Documentation of Acute Compartment Syndrome at an Academic Health-Care Center," *Journal of Bone and Joint Surgery* 87 (2005): 346–50 and Y. W. Novitsky, R. F. Sing, K. W. Kercher, and M. L. Griffo, "Prospective, Blinded Evaluation of Accuracy of Operative Reports Dictated By Surgical Residents," *The American Surgeon* 71, no. 8 (2005): 627–32.

6. K. A. Larson, E. Wiggins, and M. A. Goldfarb, "Reducing Medication Errors in a Surgical Residency Training Program," *The American Surgeon* 70, no. 5 (2004): 467–71.

7. See K. M. Gans, T. M. Lasater, R. S. Lefebvre, W. McQuade, and R. A. Carleton, "Changing Physician's Attitudes, Knowledge, and Self-Efficacy Regarding Cholesterol Screening and Management," *American Journal of Preventative Medicine* 9 (1993): 101–6 and R. Lenzi, W. F. Baile, J. Berek, A. Back, R. Buckman, L. Cohen, and P. Parker, "Design, Conduct, and Evaluation of a Communication Course for Oncology Fellows," *Journal of Cancer Education* 20, no. 3 (2005): 143–49.

8. National Coalition for Health Care, *Charting the Cost of Inaction* (Washington, D.C.: National Coalition for Healthcare, 2003).

9. M. B. Flynn, D. A. Allen, W. Browder, and R. D. Stahl, "The Operative Note as Billing Documentation: A Preliminary Report/Discussion," *The American Surgeon* 70, no. 7 (2004): 570–74.

10. Y. W. Novitsky, R. F. Sing, K. W. Kercher, and M. L. Griffo, "Prospective, Blinded Evaluation of Accuracy of Operative Reports Dictated by Surgical Residents," *The American Surgeon* 71, no. 8 (2005): 627–32.

11. A. E. Carroll, P. Tarczy-Homoch, E. O'Reilly, and D. A. Christakis, "Resident Documentation Discrepancies in a Neonatal Intensive Care Unit," *Pediatrics* 111, no. 5 (2003): 976–80.

12. B. M. Cascio, J. H. Wilckens, M. C. Ain, C. Toulson, and F. J. Frassica, "Documentation of Acute Compartment Syndrome at an Academic Health-Care Center," *Journal of Bone and Joint Surgery* 87 (2005): 346–50.

CHAPTER 2

1. A. D. Stajkovic and F. Luthans, "Self-Efficacy and Work-Related Performances: A Meta-Analysis," *Psychological Bulletin* 124, no. 2 (1998): 240–61.

CHAPTER 3

1. Provided by Navigant Consulting, Inc.
2. Provided by Navigant Consulting, Inc.

CHAPTER 4

1. H. K. Laschinger and C. Tresolini, "An Exploratory Study of Nursing and Medical Students Health Promotion Counseling Self-Efficacy," *Nurse Education Today* 19 (1999): 408–418.

CHAPTER 5

1. E. R. Lenz and L. M. Shortridge-Baggett, *Self-Efficacy in Nursing: Research and Measurement Perspectives* (New York: Springer, 2002).

CHAPTER 7

1. Jerome Groopman, *How Doctors Think* (New York: Houghton Mifflin, 2007).
2. S. M. Jex and P. D. Bliese, "Efficacy Beliefs as a Moderator of the Impact of Work-Related Stressors: A Multilevel Study," *Journal of Applied Psychology* 84, no. 3 (1999): 349–61.
3. V. Sutherland and C. L. Cooper, *De-Stressing Doctors: A Self-Management Guide* (London: Elsevier Science Limited, 2003).
4. S. Covey, *The 7 Habits of Highly Effective People: Powerful Lessons in Personal Change* (New York: Simon and Schuster, 1989).
5. Julie Morgenstern, *Never Check E-mail in the Morning and Other Unexpected Strategies for Making Your Work Life Work* (New York: Fireside Press, 2004).
6. Alec Mackenzie, *The Time Trap: The Classic Book on Time Management* (New York: Amacom Press, 1997).
7. Ibid., 223.
8. J. W. Crosby, "Ten Time Management Tips For Family Physicians," *Canadian Medical Association Journal* 170 (2004): 949–50.
9. Jennifer Bush, "Life Balance: 17 Tips from Doctors, for Doctors." Originally

published in *Family Practice and Management* (June 2001). Available online at: *www.aafp.org/fpm/20010600/60life.html.*

CHAPTER 10

1. M. M. Brown, G. C. Brown, and S. Sharma, *Evidence-Based to Value-Based Medicine* (Chicago: American Medical Association Press, 2005).

2. S. Timmermans and M. Berg, *The Gold Standard: The Challenge of Evidence-Based Medicine and Standardization in Health Care* (Philadelphia: Temple University Press, 2003).

3. *Oxford English Dictionary* (Oxford: Oxford University Press, 2005).

CHAPTER 13

1. A. J. Audet, M. M. Doty, J. Shamasdin, and S. C. Schoenbaum, *Physicians' Views on Quality of Care: Findings from The Commonwealth Fund National Survey of Physicians and Quality of Care* (New York: The Commonwealth Fund, 2005).

2. Press Ganey Associates, *Hospital Check-Up Report: Physician Perspectives on American Hospitals, 2007* (South Bend, Indiana: 2007).

CHAPTER 16

1. B. Hayward, "How Do You Define Employee Engagement?," *OPC Limited*; available online at: *www.opcuk.com/downloads/defining_employee_engagement.pdf.*

2. See OPC, "How Do You Define Employee Engagement?" (*www.opcuk.com/downloads/defining_employee_engagement.pdf*) and Patricia Soldati, "Employee Engagement: What Exactly Is It?," *Management Issues* (March 8, 2007); available online at: *www.management-issues.com/2007/3/8/opinion/employee-engagement-what-exactly-is-it.asp.*

3. Barb Sanford, "Building a Highly Engaged Workforce: How Great Managers Inspire Virtuoso Performance" (interview with Curt Coffman), *Gallup Management Journal* (2003); reproduced online at: *www.govleaders.org/gallup_article.htm.*

4. See Patricia Soldati, "Employee Engagement: What Exactly Is It?," *Management Issues* (March 8, 2007: *www.management-issues.com/2007/3/8/opinion/employee-engagement-what-exactly-is-it.asp*) and Barb Sanford, "Building a Highly

Engaged Workforce: How Great Managers Inspire Virtuoso Performance"
(interview with Curt Coffman), *Gallup Management Journal* (2003); reproduced
online at: *www.govleaders.org/gallup_article.htm.*

Index to Volumes 1 and 2

Environmental Statement

This two-volume set was printed on
100% post-consumer waste fiber.
The paper is elemental chlorine free
and was manufactured using biogas
energy. According to calculations
based on research by Environmental
Defense and other members of
the Paper Task Force, the following
environmental resources were saved:

101,412 gallons of water
19,645 pounds of greenhouse gases
141 fully grown trees
8,946 pounds of solid waste
121 million British thermal units of energy

DJ Iber Publishing, Inc. is committed
to the environment.